The Poetry Friday Anthology

OTHER POETRY ANTHOLOGIES
COMPILED BY
VARDELL AND WONG

The Poetry Friday Anthology
for Science
Grades K–5

Poems for the School Year
Integrating Science, Reading, and Language Arts
(Spring 2014)

The Poetry Friday Anthology
for Middle School
Grades 6-8

Poems for the School Year
with Connections to the Common Core
or
with Connections to the TEKS

The PoetryTagTime E-book Trio
PoetryTagTime (for K-5)
P*TAG (for teens)
Gift Tag (holiday poems)

The first-ever electronic anthologies of original poetry
for children and teens

THE POETRY FRIDAY ANTHOLOGY

Poems for the School Year
with Connections to the Common Core
K-5 Edition

218 poems by 76 poets

compiled by
Sylvia Vardell and Janet Wong

pomelo ✳ books

✳ ✳ ✳

this book is dedicated to
all the poets
in our anthologies
for their generosity and inspiration

Pomelo Books
4580 Province Line Road
Princeton, NJ 08540
www.PomeloBooks.com
info@PomeloBooks.com

Library of Congress Cataloging-in-Publication Data is available.

ISBN 978-1-937057-68-8

Please visit us:
www.PomeloBooks.com

Poems By

Joy Acey	Jacqueline Jules
Arnold Adoff	Bobbi Katz
Jaime Adoff	X. J. Kennedy
Kathi Appelt	Michele Krueger
Linda Ashman	Julie Larios
Jeannine Atkins	Irene Latham
Brod Bagert	JonArno Lawson
Carmen T. Bernier-Grand	Gail Carson Levine
Robyn Hood Black	Constance Levy
Susan Taylor Brown	Debbie Levy
Joseph Bruchac	J. Patrick Lewis
Jen Bryant	George Ella Lyon
Leslie Bulion	Guadalupe Garcia McCall
Stephanie Calmenson	Heidi Mordhorst
Deborah Chandra	Kenn Nesbitt
Cynthia Cotten	Lesléa Newman
Kristy Dempsey	Linda Sue Park
Graham Denton	Ann Whitford Paul
Rebecca Kai Dotlich	Greg Pincus
Margarita Engle	Jack Prelutsky
Betsy Franco	Mary Quattlebaum
Carole Gerber	Heidi Bee Roemer
Charles Ghigna	Michael J. Rosen
Joan Bransfield Graham	Deborah Ruddell
John Grandits	Laura Purdie Salas
Nikki Grimes	Michael Salinger
Lorie Ann Grover	Ken Slesarik
Monica Gunning	Eileen Spinelli
Mary Lee Hahn	Susan Marie Swanson
Avis Harley	Amy Ludwig VanDerwater
David L. Harrison	Lee Wardlaw
Terry Webb Harshman	Charles Waters
Juanita Havill	April Halprin Wayland
Georgia Heard	Carole Boston Weatherford
Esther Hershenhorn	Steven Withrow
Sara Holbrook	Allan Wolf
Carol-Ann Hoyte	Janet Wong
Patricia Hubbell	Jane Yolen

*"Poetry and Hums **aren't things which you get, they're things which get YOU.** And all you can do is to go where they can find you."*

꙳ A. A. Milne ꙳
The House at Pooh Corner

TABLE OF CONTENTS

What Is Poetry Friday?	8
Poetry and the Common Core	11
A Poem for Everyone: "The Most Glad-to-See Day of the Year"	21
Common Core Standards for Kindergarten	24
Poems for Kindergarten	25
Common Core Standards for First Grade	64
Poems for First Grade	65
Common Core Standards for Second Grade	104
Poems for Second Grade	105
Common Core Standards for Third Grade	144
Poems for Third Grade	145
Common Core Standards for Fourth Grade	184
Poems for Fourth Grade	185
Common Core Standards for Fifth Grade	224
Poems for Fifth Grade	225
A Poem for Everyone: "The Last Day of School"	263
Building Your Own Poetry Library	267
Copyright and Permissions	274
Title Index	275
Poet Index	279
Poem Credits	281
TGIF!	288
Acknowledgments	291
About Sylvia Vardell and Janet Wong	292

What Is Poetry Friday?

In 2006 blogger Kelly Herold brought Poetry Friday to the "kidlitosphere." Much like "casual Friday" in the corporate world, there is a perception in the world of literature that on Fridays we should relax a bit and take a moment for something special. **Why not bring the Poetry Friday concept into your classroom, taking five minutes every Friday to share a poem** and explore it a bit, connect it with children's lives, and capitalize on a teachable moment? Pausing to share a poem—and reinforce a language skill—on Poetry Friday is an easy way to infuse poetry into your current teaching practice.

On Poetry Friday, you can find blog posts that include original poems, book reviews, song lyrics, poetry curriculum tips, and more. Each Friday a different blogger volunteers to gather and host a list of poetry posts from participating blogs. For a list of participating bloggers, see *25 Children's Poetry Websites and Blogs You Need to Know* on page 269.

Yes, of course you can share poetry on other days of the week, too—and we hope that you will! But for those who are not already teaching poetry regularly, planning for Poetry Friday makes poetry sharing intentional rather than incidental. **And once you have celebrated a month of Poetry Fridays, we promise that students will be clamoring for it.**

POETRY AND THE COMMON CORE

*"Poetry is power—**power to live your life fully** and to realize your dreams. The younger we are when we start creating and articulating our experiences, the more easily we can find our path in life. The more we support children as they find their own voices, the farther they can go."*

&❦ Caroline Kennedy ❧&

Poetry and the Common Core

The new Common Core Standards provide a framework that informs instruction and include a component focused on teaching children about poetry. That provides a central focus for this book, which is first and foremost a quality anthology of original poetry for children written by 76 of today's most popular poets. Children in any state or country can enjoy, explore, and respond to these poems. However, we have also come to realize that educators, librarians, and parents are looking for guidance on how to share poetry with children and teach the skills within the curriculum as well. Thus, this book offers both: quality poetry plus curriculum-based suggestions for helping children enjoy and understand poetry more deeply.

What are the expectations outlined in the Common Core?

In sharing poetry with **kindergartners**, we capitalize on their developing knowledge of language, their joy in learning and playing with words, and their emerging understanding of how words should be spoken, spelled, read, and written. First we focus on enjoyment and understanding, then we guide students in recognizing and responding to poems. We can explore the rhythm of poetry as well as the power of rhyme and the sounds of words.

With **first graders**, we shift slightly to guide students in understanding how poets express feelings in poetry and appeal to the senses through language. We can also help them understand and identify the words and phrases poets use to communicate emotions and convey sensory experiences through poetry.

In **second grade,** we guide students in responding to the rhythm of poetry and recognizing how rhyme is used in poems. We can also explore how repetition and alliteration can help shape a poem and how meaning emerges.

In **third grade** we support students in responding to poetry in various forms, exploring narrative poems that tell stories, lyrical poems that explore questions and emotions, and humorous poems that make us groan or laugh. We help students understand how poets use lines and stanzas to build poems in distinctive ways.

In **fourth grade**, we also guide students in responding to poetry in various forms, articulating themes from key ideas and details in the poems. In sharing poetry aloud and in print, we can assist students in understanding how structural elements such as verse, rhythm, and meter help shape a poem.

Finally, in **fifth grade**, the emphasis is to help students respond to poetry in various forms, articulate themes from key ideas and details in the poems, and explain how the poem's speaker reflects upon a topic and shapes it with a particular point of view. We can guide students in understanding word meanings and how figurative language like metaphors and similes function in poetry. We can also discuss how structural elements like stanzas and line breaks help shape a poem and how visual and multimedia elements contribute to the meaning, tone, or beauty of a poem. In a variety of meaningful and participatory ways, we can celebrate poetry while gently introducing and reinforcing key skills.

The keys to remember are:

- A poem should first be enjoyed for its own sake.

- Presenting poems in participatory ways through various choral strategies gets your learner "into the poem."

- The main idea is to help your learner see and hear the poetic elements after enjoying the poem through multiple readings—and to come through the "back door" to skills.

READING POETRY ALOUD

A guiding principle of this book is that **poetry is meant to be read aloud**. As the award-winning poet Eve Merriam noted, "It's easier to savor the flavor of the words as they roll around in your mouth for your ears to enjoy." Like song lyrics that sit quietly on the page, the music of poetry comes alive when spoken and shared. Reading aloud is also the ideal way to approach poetry instruction.

The more children hear, read, say, and experience the poem, the more they internalize the sounds, words, and meanings of the poem and begin to notice the mechanics and artistry of poetry.

Here are some tips to help you read aloud effectively:

- Be sure to *say the title and author* of the poem.

- If possible, *display the words of the poem* while you read it aloud.

- Be sure to *enunciate each word* distinctly and to check uncertain pronunciations beforehand.

- *Glance at the audience* occasionally.

- *Add to the effect with a portable microphone* using a microphone app.

Why Poetry?

When we think about what poetry does for children—and in just a few minutes of sharing on a regular basis—it's a pretty impressive list. Author and literacy expert Mem Fox noted, "Rhymers will be readers; it's that simple." Here are some key benefits of sharing poetry with children:

- Poetry reinforces word sounds, rimes, rhymes, patterns, and pronunciation—think phonics!

- Poetry introduces new vocabulary and figurative language, as well as examples of synonyms, antonyms, puns, word play, and coining of new words and expressions.

- Poetry is rich in imagery that stimulates the imagination.

- Poetry often includes sensory language that communicates to children the senses of sight, smell, touch, taste, and hearing.

- Poetry offers an emotional connection and can reflect and elicit powerful and deeply felt moments.

- Poetry provides practice for oral language development, listening, and oral fluency, as well as a bridge to understanding the written word.

- Poetry has pedagogical uses across the curriculum (e.g., building science concepts, reinforcing historical themes, adding motivation to math lessons), making it an effective tool for connecting with nonfiction.

- Poetry can heighten awareness of the use of mechanical conventions, from spacing and margins to commas and quotation marks.

- Poetry is accessible to a wide range of reading abilities and language learning skill levels.

- Poetry has a long shelf life, and poems can be revisited again and again, prompting different responses at different ages and stages.

Poetry Breaks

Whether you introduce a poem at the beginning of the day, when transitioning to lunch or a break, or when wrapping things up, "breaking" for poetry provides a moment to refresh and engage. Of course, this doesn't mean that a more in-depth study of poetry is not a good idea. It is. But for the average teacher or librarian, consistently sharing a five-minute poem break is an effective practice. Communicate to students that a poetry break is about to begin by using a sign, bell, signal, or chime announcing "Poetry Break!"

Maximizing the Benefit of the Take 5 Activities

Our Take 5 activities rely heavily on reading the poem aloud—and in multiple ways—as well as talking about the poem and following up with more oral reading of more poetry. We also provide specific guidelines for how to approach each poem aloud. Here are a few guidelines, drawn from the work of Jack Collom and Sheryl Noethe in *Poetry Everywhere*, that might be helpful.

- Be yourself. You needn't and shouldn't show reverence for poetry by means of an artificially dignified atmosphere.

- Energy is the key—but it shouldn't be forced. A brisk pace is good, as as long as you slow down when the situation needs it.

- Practice reading with pauses at the ends of lines and in other places. Think about how this affects your students' understanding of a poem.

- It's helpful to admit your own errors and ignorance. Poetry can be ambiguous and poetry rules are sometimes unclear.

- Don't worry. Decide what you're going to do and go for it. Relax and concentrate. Freely intersperse humor and seriousness. Have fun!

---

3 Fun and Easy Ways to Celebrate Poetry

"Poetry Celebrations" give your students something to look forward to and can provide opportunities for child participation. For hundreds of additional suggestions and ideas, consult *The Poetry Teacher's Book of Lists* by Sylvia Vardell.

1. If audio announcements are made on a regular basis, **encourage children to try a performance reading** with sound effects or musical instruments.

2. Read poems for birthdays, such as **birthday poems** or favorite poems of the birthday child. Invite families to donate poetry books in honor of the birthday child.

3. **Share a poem about food while children enjoy a snack** at snack time, Mother's Day Tea, or Open House. Choose poems from an e-book, such as *PoetryTagTime*, and project the poems for all to see during the event.

How to Use the Take 5 Box

Tip #1: This tip provides an easy suggestion for how to make the poem come alive as you read it aloud by pairing the poem with a prop, adding gestures or movement, trying specific dramatic reading techniques, singing the poem to a certain tune, and so on.

Tip #3: You'll find a fun discussion prompt here, tailored to fit the poem. It's usually an open-ended question with no single, correct answer. Encourage diversity in responses!

Tip #4: We designed this tip to connect the poem to a specific language arts or poetry skill or concept such as rhyme, repetition, rhythm, alliteration, or onomatopoeia. This is also where we point out poetry forms (e.g., cinquain, haiku, tanka, acrostic, diamante) and explain techniques like personification and simile.

Take 5!

1. Pose the class together for an informal group photograph taken with your camera, phone, or iPad, and read this poem aloud before you snap the photo. Say *fleas!*

2. **Read the poem aloud again and invite students to join in on saying CHEESE! and FLEAS!** Alert them to the poet's use of capital letters for greater emphasis.

3. For discussion: *What makes a school or family photo funny?*

4. Poets use all kinds of tools to add interest and variety to a poem. Here, **the poet uses capital letters to indicate when words should receive greater emphasis**.

5. Another occasion that often calls for photos is a choir performance like the one depicted in **"My Kindergarten Choir" by Avis Harley** (Kindergarten, Week 16, page 42).

Tip #2: This tip suggests how to engage children in reading the poem aloud with you. One example is echo reading in which you ask students to repeat certain words or lines after you. Note: when leading an echo reading, keep the pace moving so the echo reading won't interrupt the poem to the point of distraction.

Tip #5: In this tip we share other related poem titles and poetry book titles that connect well with the featured poem. You can find additional poetry connections and cross-genre connections at the **Poetry Friday Anthology blog** and at the **Poetry for Children blog**. See the list *25 Children's Poetry Web Sites and Blogs You Need to Know* on page 269 for these and other blog addresses.

Choral Reading

For each poem, we provide suggestions for how to invite students to participate in reading the poem aloud. If you want to experiment with even more ways of bringing the poem to life, here are additional strategies for repeated reading. As you experiment with these strategies, it will become obvious that they can be combined and overlapped. Often the poem itself will "show" you how to perform it if you study the lines and their arrangement on the page. And when you invite children to participate in poem performance, you will find that they will have ideas about how to try a poem this way or that way. Follow their lead!

Unison and echo reading
An adult reads the poem aloud first. Then everyone joins in to read the poem in unison. You can adapt this approach with "echo" reading of some poems, in which children repeat each line after you read it.

Refrains and repeated words
The adult leads the poem reading, but children participate in a word, phrase, or refrain that is repeated.

Motion and movement
Invite listeners to join in with designated motions or gestures.

Groups
Divide your class into two or more groups to recite key words or stanzas.

Solos
Individual children volunteer for solo lines. (The key word is "volunteer.") Many list poems work well in this format.

Singing
Perhaps the most entertaining form of choral reading is singing poems. It's not difficult and is irresistible fun. You simply sing poems by adapting those that have a strong, rhythmic beat to familiar tunes that have the same beat or meter, such as "Row, Row, Row Your Boat."

Additional Creative Alternatives for Poem-Sharing

- Use props and physical objects referenced in the poem.
- Pantomime motions or emotions that fit the poem.
- Use simple movements like a tap for poems with a regular rhythm.
- Create simple sound effects as the background for a poem reading.
- Add a musical soundtrack or muted video backdrop.
- Draw a simple picture, as in Pictionary, while reading the poem.
- Perform poem using signing (American Sign Language).
- Stage a *tableau*, a frozen moment of a poem posed as a scene.

Share a poem every Friday, and over the course of the school year you will have introduced 36 different original poems by contemporary poets on some of the most popular themes and topics in poetry for young people.

Each week has a designated theme that crosses all levels, K-5. This provides a school-wide connection as each grade enjoys a different poem on the same topic.

Themes and topics begin with school itself and also include fun and games, pets, weather, food, families, communities, holidays, the human body, art, friendship, kindness, science and technology, music and dance, summer vacation, and rhythm, rhyme, repetition, metaphor, simile, and personification.

You will find multiple connections across the curriculum in science, social studies, art, and music, with endless possibilities for collaboration and expansion.

Lexiles and Levels

The readability level of poems varies greatly since poetry doesn't easily fit the use of Lexiles and levels. Simple poems can have very sophisticated vocabulary and long poems can use simple language. Determining Lexile levels is based on a variety of factors, such as how long the sentences are and how unusual the words are, as well as on the use of basic punctuation. The nursery rhyme "Little Jack Horner," for example, is written at the same eighth grade level as Robert Frost's classic poem "Stopping by Woods on a Snowy Evening." But clearly they are significantly different works. The power lies in a poem's meaning and in the distinctive ways the poet uses and arranges words. With these principles in mind, **this anthology presents poems for each grade level selected for their relevance, interest, and appropriateness for each grade.**

Conclusion

Read these poems aloud so that students of all abilities and language learning levels can participate in the poem. Display the words so that students can have visual as well as aural reinforcement. Invite students to join in saying words and reading the text as they make the poem their own. Talk about the poems and invite students to share what they notice, then build on their knowledge to expand that skills base.

Link the poems with more poems, more poets, and more poetry books. Infuse poem-sharing throughout the day and throughout the curriculum. Mark this book up with notes about your students' responses to individual poems. **And don't be surprised if it's a wonderful poem moment that students remember most vividly at the end of the school year!**

WHICH POEMS SHOULD WE READ?

We offer a set of 36 poems—a poem-a-week for the nine months of the typical school year—for each grade level and have designed poem-specific, skill-based, and developmentally appropriate activities for each weekly poem.

Our goal is to provide support for educators and parents who might be unfamiliar with today's poetry for young people and might need guidance in how to begin. For each poem you share, we suggest another poem from the book that is related in some way.

Feel free to share any and all of the poems with the students you teach at any time, in any order, and in any way you like.

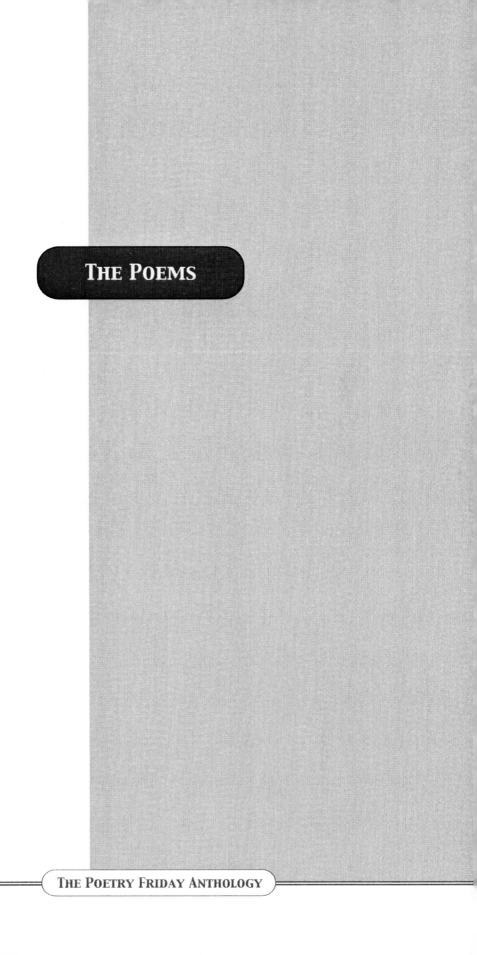

THE POEMS

THE MOST GLAD-TO-SEE DAY OF THE YEAR
by **Allan Wolf**

My favorite, special, most glad-to-see day,
the day I consider the best.
The day when I really get carried away.
The top day all year! Can you guess?

It isn't my birthday. It isn't Thanksgiving.
And no, it's not Hanukkah, Christmas, and all.
It's not Halloween that makes life so worth living.
My day happens Spring, Summer, Winter, and Fall.

It's not a one-timer. My day never ends.
It's the first, second, middle, and last.
It is here, holy cow! It is new. It is now.
It is not in the future or past.

I'll give you the answer: My day is . . . Today!
There's no waiting in line. There is no long delay.
What yesterday was and tomorrow will be,
Today's the most wonderful day for me.

*"Poetry in the classroom **is like a bouncing ball** but with words jumping around the page creating imagination and movement."*

꩜ Paige Bentley-Flannery ꩜

POEMS FOR KINDERGARTEN

COMMON CORE STANDARDS
FOR KINDERGARTEN (RL.K.5)

In sharing poetry with kindergartners, we capitalize on their developing knowledge of language, their joy in learning and playing with words, and their emerging understanding of how words should be spoken, spelled, read, and written.

First we focus on enjoyment and understanding, then we guide students in recognizing and responding to poems.

We can explore the rhythm of poetry as well as the power of rhyme and the sounds of words.

In fun and participatory ways, we can celebrate poetry while gently introducing and reinforcing key skills.

week 1	School	Happy Song for the First Day of School *by Patricia Hubbell*
week 2	More School	Kindergarten Kid *by Stephanie Calmenson*
week 3	Fun & Games	Let's Hop Around Like Kangaroos *by Allan Wolf*
week 4	Pets	Petting Zoo *by Laura Purdie Salas*
week 5	More Pets	Oh Man! *by David L. Harrison*
week 6	On the Ground	The World's Most Ancient Ant *by Jack Prelutsky*
week 7	In the Water	Tadpole Wishes *by Terry Webb Harshman*
week 8	In the Air	Bluejay Sings Two Different Songs *by Mary Lee Hahn*
week 9	Weather	Teddy Wear *by Graham Denton*
week 10	Food	Who Invented Cookies? *by Joan Bransfield Graham*
week 11	More Food	Sack Lunch *by Charles Waters*
week 12	House & Home	Cabbage House *by Terry Webb Harshman*
week 13	Families	Who's Who *by Julie Larios*
week 14	Community	Mrs. Betty *by Rebecca Kai Dotlich*
week 15	Stuff We Love	Bubble Bath *by Sara Holbrook*
week 16	Holidays	My Kindergarten Choir *by Avis Harley*
week 17	Time Together	Stormy Day *by Rebecca Kai Dotlich*
week 18	Human Body	Tooth *by Amy Ludwig VanDerwater*
week 19	More Human Body	I Sit On My Bottom *by Michael Salinger*
week 20	Art & Colors	Waiting *by Lorie Ann Grover*
week 21	Love & Friendship	Frog and Toad *by J. Patrick Lewis*
week 22	A Kinder Place	Something I Did *by Janet Wong*
week 23	Exploring	Trouble on the Trail *by Robyn Hood Black*
week 24	Science & Tech	They Call It "Science" *by Stephanie Calmenson*
week 25	Song & Dance	Keys *by Joy Acey*
week 26	Nonsense	How Many Slams Are in an Old Screen Door? *by Allan Wolf*
week 27	World of Words	Animal Talk *by Charles Ghigna*
week 28	Books	The Book *by Stephanie Calmenson*
week 29	Poetry Poems	Poems Are Out of This World *by Charles Ghigna*
week 30	RR&R	Loose Tooth, Whose Tooth? *by Carole Boston Weatherford*
week 31	Different Forms	Crayons *by Ann Whitford Paul*
week 32	Metaphor & Simile	My Bike *by Julie Larios*
week 33	Personification	No Wonder *by Constance Levy*
week 34	On the Move	Bouncing Along *by Kristy Dempsey*
week 35	Summer Vacation	No Way! *by David L. Harrison*
week 36	Looking Forward	Moving Up Day *by Janet Wong*

*"Lizards dancing with birds? No problem. **The world is full of wonders, says Poetry**, and your only job is to be able to see those wonders, to feel them, and to try to communicate them."*

Joyce Sidman

HAPPY SONG FOR THE FIRST DAY OF SCHOOL
by Patricia Hubbell

Take 5!

1. As you read this poem aloud, **snap your fingers** after reading "snappy" and keep snapping a regular beat throughout the poem.

2. **Invite students to echo read** the poem, repeating each line after you read it aloud.

3. For discussion: *How do you make a new friend?*

4. **See if students can identify pairs of rhyming words**, or "words that sound alike" (*happy/snappy; tip/hip; day/hooray; tootle/oodle; end/friend*). Say the pairs of words out loud together, then repeat, inviting students to complete each pairing. Then share the whole poem aloud again.

5. Share another rousing school poem, **"Ready" by Joan Bransfield Graham** (in this book under 1st Grade, Week 1, page 67) or a poem from *Stampede* by Laura Purdie Salas.

It's my
Happy
Snappy
Tip-top
Day

Tootle
Oodle
Hip
Hooray!

I wish
This day
Would never
End—

I've just
Made a
Brand-new
Friend!

KINDERGARTEN KID
by Stephanie Calmenson

I'm a Kindergarten Kid,
And there's lots that I can do.
Come into my classroom.
I'll show some things to you.

Here's our reading corner.
I read a brand new book today.
It was a silly one about a horse,
Who said "Moo!" instead of "Neigh."

Our building center's here.
I made a tower that was tall.
It wiggled and it wobbled.
But it didn't ever fall!

Here's our writing center.
I can write my a, b, c's.
Over here is math.
I know my 1, 2, 3's.

These are our pet guinea pigs.
We named them Peach and Plum.
Here's our cooking corner.
We made oatmeal cookies—yum!

I'm a Kindergarten Kid,
And there's lots that I can do.
Will you show me your room,
And the things you like to do?

Take 5!

1. As you read the poem aloud, walk around the classroom like a tour guide and **point to areas as they are mentioned** in the poem.

2. Read the poem again and **invite students to raise their hands whenever you say the word *here* or *here's*.**

3. For discussion: ***What are your favorite areas in our classroom?***

4. Read the poem aloud again and pause dramatically before the last word in each stanza. **See if the students can guess the rhyming word to end each stanza.** If needed, point out that one clue is the rhyming word earlier in the stanza, at the end of the second line.

5. Share a poem about different ways to spend recess, **"Recess" by Avis Harley** (2nd Grade, Week 2, page 108) or a poem from *Counting Our Way to the 100th Day!* by Betsy Franco.

LET'S HOP AROUND LIKE KANGAROOS
by **Allan Wolf**

Take 5!

1. As you read the poem aloud, **pantomime the motions mentioned in each stanza** of the poem: hopping, clinking (maybe a pen against a cup), and marching.

2. Read the poem aloud again and **invite students to hop in place** every time *kanga* or *kangaroo* pops up. Cue students by raising your hand or hopping.

3. For discussion: *What else might kangaroos try to do?*

4. Read the poem again, inviting students to hop, clink, and march with you. **Point out how the poet repeats words like *kanga, hop*, and *march* over and over again.** Repetition is a key ingredient in creating poems.

5. Share a poem that blends a kangaroo with a rooster, **"The Kangarooster" by Jack Prelutsky** (4th Grade, Week 30, page 216).

Let's hop around like kangaroos!
A kanga-me. A kanga-you.
Let's hop around like kangas do.
Let's hop like kangaroos.

Let's clink a pot. Let's clank a pan.
Let's clunk on metal kanga cans.
Let's clang like only kangas can.
Let's clang like kangaroos.

Let's march our feet and clap our hands.
Let's form a kanga marching band
and march our way to Kanga-land.
Let's march like kangaroos.

And you can be a kanga too!

PETTING ZOO
by **Laura Purdie Salas**

Bossy goats,
Floppy dogs,
Silky bunnies,
Bristly hogs.

Milk a cow,
Find a nest.
I like cuddling
Kittens best!

Take 5!

1. Before reading the poem, **ask students to name animals** they might encounter at a petting zoo. Share the poem emphasizing each animal name.

2. Read the poem aloud again and **invite students to make the corresponding animal noises**.

3. For discussion: *What is your favorite animal from this poem?* What kinds of animals might be found in a nest?

4. Poets love to play with words. Sometimes they'll use a word just because they like the sound of it or the way it makes a picture in their minds. **Do the words *bossy, floppy, silky*, and *bristly* make a picture in your mind?** Talk about those pictures together.

5. Share another poem about kittens, **"All Worn Out" by Kristy Dempsey** (2nd Grade, Week 5, page 111).

OH MAN!
by **David L. Harrison**

I really want
that porcupine.

(But Daddy says no.)

We'd get along
just fine.

(But Mommy says no.)

I wish that porcupine
was mine.

(He won't be though.)

Take 5!

1. Read the poem aloud using **a whispering voice for the lines in parentheses**.

2. Read the poem aloud again, **pausing after the word *says*,** so students can chime in with the word *no*.

3. For discussion: ***What might happen if Daddy and Mommy said yes to a porcupine pet?***

4. Ask students what they notice about the poem and how it sounds. Responses may include things like the repetition of the words *porcupine* or *no*. Accept all answers and piggyback on their responses to highlight how **the poet REPEATS words or phrases to make the poem sound like a poem.**

5. Share another poem about pets by **David Harrison, "My Pet"** (2nd Grade, Week 4, page 110) or another poem about a porcupine pet, **"My Porcupine Is Feeling Fine" by Kenn Nesbitt** (4th Grade, Week 4, page 190).

THE WORLD'S MOST ANCIENT ANT
by Jack Prelutsky

I, the world's most ancient ant,
Am growing frail and weak.
What other ants can do, I can't—
I am an ant antique.

Take 5!

1. Discuss the meanings of the words *ancient, frail, antique*—and then read the poem aloud **slowly, as if you were very, very OLD**. Pause for extra emphasis between the words *ant* and *antique* in the last line.

2. Read the poem again and this time **invite students to crawl like ancient ants**, moving VERY slowly while you read aloud.

3. For discussion: *How many words can you think of that have* ant *in them?* (Pants, plant, cantaloupe, fantastic.)

4. Challenge students to **identify some of the words in this poem with the long or short *a* sounds**: *ancient, ant, am, frail, and, ants, can, can't, an, antique*. Talk about how repeating sounds helps make a poem a poem.

5. Share another insect poem such as **"Gnat and Flea" by J. Patrick Lewis** (1st Grade, Week 27, page 93) or more poems by Jack Prelutsky from books like *I've Lost My Hippopotamus.*

TADPOLE WISHES
by **Terry Webb Harshman**

In the pond where
   cattails grow,
tiny tadpoles
   come and go,

swimming happily
   like fish.
But I wonder . . .
   do they *wish*

for little legs
   and feet to sprout
so they can all
   leapfrog about?

Take 5!

1. Talk about possibly unfamiliar words like *cattails, tadpoles,* and *leapfrog.* Then read the poem aloud while you **play an audio recording of pond sounds** in the background, available via SoundCloud.com (Pond Sounds).

2. Read the poem again, inviting students to **add simple hand motions** while you read: hands moving up (cattails growing in the first stanza), hands together moving back and forth (for swimming happily in the second stanza) and fingers walking then leaping on the opposite palm (for the final stanza).

3. For discussion: *What other wishes might tadpoles have?*

4. **Identify words that rhyme** (*grow/go; fish/wish; sprout/ about*). Read the poem out loud again and invite students to make a leapfrog motion with their hands when they hear a rhyme (*go, wish, about*).

5. Share another poem about frogs, **"Frog and Toad" by J. Patrick Lewis** (Kindergarten, Week 21, page 47).

BLUEJAY SINGS TWO DIFFERENT SONGS
by **Mary Lee Hahn**

tweedle, tweedle
round and flutey:
"You're a beauty!"

jay-jay-jay
sharp and rusty:
"Cat's not trusty!"

Take 5!

1. **Read the two stanzas of this poem in opposite ways:** the first stanza with a high and happy voice, the second with a low and scratchy voice.

2. **Invite students to echo read** the poem, repeating each line after you read it aloud.

3. For discussion: *What might the cat in this poem say back to the bluejay?*

4. The repeated sound words and the rhyming pairs (*flutey/beauty; rusty/trusty*) are the key building blocks for this poem. **Say the word pairs together and then read the whole poem aloud again.** Discuss the poet's use of the "made-up" words *flutey* and *trusty*. Poets can do that!

5. Share another poem about birds such as **"Bluebirds" by Jen Bryant** (3rd Grade, Week 8, page 154) or a poem from *Today at the Bluebird Café* by Deborah Ruddell.

Take 5!

1. Feeling brave? **You can sing this poem to the tune of "O, Tannenbaum"** ("Oh, Christmas Tree"). Or simply read the poem holding a teddy bear.

2. Sing or say this poem again, **inviting students to pretend to be hot** in the first stanza and cold in the second stanza.

3. For discussion: *What do teddy bears wish?*

4. **Invite students to tap the rhythm of the poem** as you share it (or sing it) again. Like a composer with the notes of a song, poets give their poems a beat, too.

5. Share another poem about weather, **"Why Does Weather?" by Mary Quattlebaum** (2nd Grade, Week 9, page 115).

TEDDY WEAR
by **Graham Denton**

On summer nights I'm glad I'm not
my hairy Teddy bear;
I really would feel far too hot
if I had all that fur!

But when the winter's hard to bear
and I am cold in bed,
well, then, oh *how* I wish I were
as furry as my Ted!

WHO INVENTED COOKIES?
by **Joan Bransfield Graham**

What clever, hungry person
took little dabs of dough,
spooned them out on pans to bake
and lined them up—just so . . .

Then popped them in the oven
to blossom soft and gooey,
turning into tasty treats,
all fragrant, warm and chewy?

So when we list inventions,
um-m, this is one to savor—
guess it didn't change the world
but, WOW, it gave it flavor!

Take 5!

1. Discuss possibly unfamiliar words (*clever, dabs, blossom, fragrant, savor*). Then, as you read the poem aloud, **pantomime the actions in the poem.**

2. Invite students to join you in a second reading by **pointing to their heads when you say the word *clever*** and saying *WOW* in the final stanza. Pause before the word to cue them to their turn.

3. For discussion: ***What kinds of cookies are your favorites?***

4. **Talk about the steps for making cookies** that are suggested in the poem (spooning dabs of dough on pans, popping them in the oven, eating them). The directions may be more exact in a recipe, but the rhyming of the poem makes it very fun to say over and over again.

5. Connect this poem with a poem about birthday cakes, **"Appy Birthday" by April Halprin Wayland** (2nd Grade, Week 24, page 130), or with "Grandmother's Almond Cookies" by Janet Wong in *A Suitcase of Seaweed*.

SACK LUNCH
by **Charles Waters**

Whole wheat oatmeal bread,
Homemade grape jelly,
Crunchy peanut butter—
A rumble in my belly.

Double chocolate cupcakes—
What a perfect snack!
Ten tiny carrot sticks?
I'd rather give that back.

Take 5!

1. **Bring a paper bag or lunch kit and put a copy of "Sack Lunch" inside it.** Then open the bag and remove the poem before reading it aloud.

2. **Next, invite students to echo read** each line after you, one line at a time.

3. For discussion: *What are your favorite foods for lunches and snacks?*

4. **Show how rhyming words help turn this "list" of foods into a poem.** Ask students: What are the words that rhyme (*jelly/belly; snack/back*)? Read the poem aloud again, but pause before the second word in each rhyming pair and wait for the students to chime in with the correct response (*belly, back*).

4. For another poem with peanut butter in it, share **"Snack Rules" by Robyn Hood Black** (1st Grade, Week 10, page 76).

CABBAGE HOUSE
by **Terry Webb Harshman**

My house is round.
  My house is green,
    with lots of layers
      in between.

My house is safe.
  My house is sound.
    It's anchored firmly
      to the ground.

If I need room,
  I eat a wall.
    It doesn't hurt
      my house at all.

This common cabbage,
  round and firm—
    princely palace
      to a *worm.*

Take 5!

1. Introduce unfamiliar words like *layers, sound* (which you can introduce as part of the phrase *safe and sound*), and *anchored.* Then add a bit of fun to sharing this poem with a "poetry prop"— **show a cabbage or a gummy worm before reading the poem aloud.**

2. In sharing the poem aloud again, **students can say the phrase *my house* each time it occurs.** Cue students by raising your hand or pointing to your ear.

3. For discussion: **What is your house or home like?**

4. Read the poem aloud again and ask students: **How many times do you hear the phrase *my house* in this poem?** (Five.) Repeating key words and phrases (like *my house*) helps build a poem and can add to the distinctive rhythm of the lines.

5. Share another poem with worms, **"When the Rain Falls" by Susan Taylor Brown** (4th Grade, Week 9, page 195).

WHO'S WHO
by **Julie Larios**

Noodle and Toodle,
Toodle and Nood,
both of them babies
and both of them rude,
both plump as piglets
and both of them stinky,
both of them bawling,
burpish and blinky—
How can their mother
tell which one is which?
Well,
Noodle likes scratching
and Tood likes to itch.

Take 5!

1. **Add exaggerated facial expressions** for *rude, stinky, bawling,* and *blinky* when reading this poem aloud.

2. **Next, invite students to echo** each line after you, repeating one line at a time as you read the poem aloud again.

3. For discussion: ***What is the difference between the words*** **itch** ***and*** **scratch?** Talk about having an itch that you can't reach to scratch or that you're not supposed to scratch.

4. **This poem is a good example of humorous poetry. Why is this funny? Ask the students!** Responses will vary, but might include: the description of the babies (*stinky, burpish*) or the babies' names (*Noodle/Nood; Toodle/Tood*). The poet uses several elements, but especially the sounds of their silly names, to add humor to the poem.

5. Share another poem about *pushy, rude,* and *greedy* little ones in **"Litter's Littlest" by Avis Harley** (1st Grade, Week 5, page 71).

MRS. BETTY
by Rebecca Kai Dotlich

Knock, knock!
Who's there?

It's Mrs. Betty!

She brought us a pot
of homemade
spaghetti!

Take 5!

1. Just before reading this poem aloud, **knock loudly twice** on a nearby surface.

2. Read the poem out loud again, and this time **coach the students to say the second line, "Who's there?"** Pause dramatically before and after that line.

3. For discussion: *What do neighbors share with each other?*

4. Students may already be familiar with jokes that begin *Knock, knock. Who's there?* (although they're not always the best joke tellers). **Point out that sometimes poets borrow patterns from other things like jokes and songs to create a new poem.**

5. Another poem about a helpful neighbor is **"The Breakfast Boss" by Janet Wong** (3rd Grade, Week 13, page 159).

BUBBLE BATH
by **Sara Holbrook**

Tubby hands
meet
tubby feet.
Plop!
I take a
bubbly seat.
Water dribbles.
Tubby splash.
Soapy scribbles.
Tubby bath.
Tickly bubbles.
Tubby laugh.
Tubby swim.
Tubby grin.
Tubby pour.
Tubby. Scrubby.
Tubby.
More!

Take 5!

1 If possible, **bring a bath toy like a rubber ducky or a bar of soap as a poetry prop** to show before reading this poem aloud.

2. Read the poem aloud again and **lift your prop (ducky or soap) every time the word _tubby_ appears** to cue students to say it out loud with you (ten times!).

3. For discussion: **_What's best and worst about bath time?_** (Bath toys, getting clean, shampoo in your eyes.)

4. **What a terrific example of how poets use repetition to create a poem.** This poet also includes many words that sound like _tubby_. See which ones the students can find (_bubbly, scrubby_; perhaps _dribble_ with a double _b_ or _soapy_ and _tickly_ ending in _y_). Then share the poem out loud again.

5. Compare this poem about bath time with how fish live in water with **"Fish" by Joy Acey** (1st Grade, Week 4, page 70).

MY KINDERGARTEN CHOIR
by **Avis Harley**

My aunt and uncle, mom and dad,
have come to hear my choir.
I'm standing on the bench behind
the kids who sing up higher.

It's hard to see beyond the lights
what row my folks are in,
but if I wave they'll find me quick
before the songs begin.

Take 5!

1. **As you read this poem aloud, stand up tall, then taller,** as if craning to see around tall people. Wave when you read the final two lines.

2. Read the poem out loud again and this time **invite the students to wave at you when you read the word *wave*.**

3. For discussion: ***Do you like to be the star of the show or help behind the scenes?***

4. This poem has a strong rhythm. **You can read it aloud again, guiding students to tap the rhythm of each line.** It's a poem that tells a story (about singing in a choir), but it does it with rhymes and a regular beat.

5. Ready for another poem about performing? Share **Brod Bagert's "Your Chance to Dance"** (1st Grade, Week 25, page 91).

STORMY DAY
by Rebecca Kai Dotlich

Everyone sits side by side.
We're cozy here.
It's cold outside.

Hey you, storm!
Until you're done,
we're having fun with
everyone!

Take 5!

1. **Read this poem aloud while sitting in the middle of a group of stuffed animals** that you have squished around you, sharing your chair or bench.

2. For a choral reading, **coach the students to say the line *Hey you, storm!*** Read the poem aloud again and pause for their unison line.

3. For discussion: *What do you do to feel safe during a storm?*

4. In these six brief lines, the poet paints a picture of a group sticking together to wait out a storm. Four lines rhyme to tie the poem together. **Ask the students to figure out which words/lines rhyme** (*side/outside; done/everyone*).

5. Share another poem about storms, **"Wondering" by Cynthia Cotten** (3rd Grade, Week 9, page 155).

TOOTH
by Amy Ludwig VanDerwater

Wiggle.
Wiggle.

Bite.
Bite.

I will pull
it out

tonight!

Take 5!

1. **Bring a toothbrush as a prop** to set the stage, and then read this poem aloud slowly and with dramatic pauses before each stanza.

2. **Break the students into two groups,** one to say the lines *Wiggle. / Wiggle.* and one to say the lines *Bite. / Bite.* Read the poem aloud again with student participation. Point to each group with your toothbrush pointer!

3. Invite the students to **share their own tooth-losing stories.**

4. **This poem has such a strong rhythm, it could be yelled on the playground or chanted while jumping rope.** For contrast, follow up by sharing the nonfiction picture book *The Tooth Book* by Edward Miller.

5. For another tooth poem by **Amy Ludwig VanDerwater**, read **"Baby Tooth"** (1st Grade, Week 18, page 84).

I SIT ON MY BOTTOM
by **Michael Salinger**

I sit on my bottom
I stand on my feet
My belly gets
The food that I eat
My eyes see the world
My hands reach and grab
My knees bend and jump
My mouth likes to gab
My heart pumps my blood
My lungs breathe in air
My brain makes things run
I have a liver somewhere
All these bits and pieces
Even some you can't see
All linked up together
Are what make up . . . me.

Take 5!

1. **This is a poem that lends itself perfectly to full-body involvement while reading it aloud,** pointing to body parts mentioned in the poem while sitting, bending, grabbing, and so on.

2. **Read the poem aloud again, inviting students to sit and stand and mimic you** in motions and actions that correspond with the poem.

3. For discussion: *Name other body parts and what they do, like nose, ears, and elbows.*

4. Alternating lines end with rhyming words in this poem. Pause before the final rhyming word in each pair and **challenge students to complete the rhyme** (*eat, gab, [some]where, me*). *Gab* may need explaining.

5. Follow up with a poem about sneezing, **"Kerchoo!" by Cynthia Cotten** (1st Grade, Week 19, page 85).

WAITING
by Lorie Ann Grover

Pots of paint wait for
my brush to gloop their color
on wide white paper.

Take 5!

1. **Before reading this poem aloud, hold up a paint brush** and ask students to guess what this poem is about. Read the words of the last line very slowly.

2. **Read the poem aloud again and invite students to say the word *gloop*** in the poem. Pause beforehand and cue them by waving the paintbrush.

3. For discussion: *What do you like to paint?*

4. Sometimes poems rhyme and sometimes they don't. In this case, **the poem doesn't rhyme, but it is full of interesting sounds.** Challenge the students to point them out, like the repeated *p* in *pots of paint*, the *w* in *wide white*, and the unusual word *gloop*.

5. Follow up with another poem about making art, **"Clay Time" by Terry Webb Harshman** (1st Grade, Week 20, page 86).

FROG AND TOAD
by J. Patrick Lewis

The look-alike of *frog* is *toad;*
They have a similar dress code.
A *frog* has skin that's smooth and slimy;
A *toad*'s complexion's warty and dry;
A *frog* would like to kiss a princess;
A *toad* prefers to kiss a fly.

Take 5!

1. After reading this poem aloud, **show images of frogs and toads** to see them side by side. One example from the Web is at allaboutfrogs.org/weird/general/frogtoad.html.

2. **Next, divide the students into two groups**—one to say the word *frog* as it occurs in the poem and one to say *toad*. Read the poem aloud again and point to the frog or toad image (from above) to cue students to participate.

3. For discussion: *How are frogs and toads alike and different?*

4. **Sometimes poets weave facts into their poems.** Guide students in noting what information we learn about frogs and toads in this poem.

5. Share another poem *as warty as a toad*, **"Outer Spaceman" by Julie Larios** (2nd Grade, Week 32, page 138).

SOMETHING I DID
by **Janet Wong**

Something I did
made Alex
not like me.
Something I did—
but what?
If Alex would tell me,
if Alex would say—
then maybe
we'd fix things
and
we could play
together
at recess
like we used to do.
What did I do wrong?
I wish I knew.

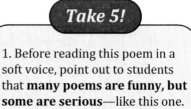

Take 5!

1. Before reading this poem in a soft voice, point out to students that **many poems are funny, but some are serious**—like this one.

2. Read the poem aloud again and **invite students to say the last line together**.

3. For discussion: *How do you know if you've hurt someone's feelings?*

4. In this poem the poet repeated *Something I did.* **Sometimes a poet uses repetition not just to enhance the sound of the poem, but to emphasize meaning.**

5. Follow up with another thoughtful poem about friendship, **"See-Saw" by Graham Denton** (1st Grade, Week 32, page 98).

TROUBLE ON THE TRAIL
by **Robyn Hood Black**

The woods are great and everything,
but now I feel an itch.

My arms are turning kind of red;
my body wants to twitch.

You think that's poison ivy there?
Now that would be some joke.

You don't? Oh, good. But what was that?
You think it's poison oak.

Take 5!

1. **Read this poem aloud while pantomiming itching,** twitching, and scratching periodically.

2. In repeated readings, **coach the students to say** *But what was that?* in the final stanza. Cue them by cupping your hand behind your ear.

3. **Be open to students sharing two or three stories about their own experiences** with rashes and allergies.

4. **Help students find the rhyming pairs that occur at the ends of the stanzas** (*itch/twitch; joke/oak*). Then read the poem aloud again, pointing to the rhyming word as students chime in to complete each rhyme.

5. Follow up by sharing **Julie Larios's poem, "Who's Who?"** (Kindergarten, Week 13, page 39).

THEY CALL IT "SCIENCE"
by Stephanie Calmenson

They call it science.
I call it why-ence.
Why is the sky blue?
Why do I look like me and not like you?
Why can't I see the sun at night?
When water turns to snow, why is it white?
Why isn't there butter in a butterfly?
Why don't they call it why-ence?
I like to ask "WHY?"!

Take 5!

1. **Create a simple sign or card with the word *why* on it.** Show it each time the word appears as you read the poem aloud. Pause dramatically before each line.

2. Read the poem aloud again and **invite students to say the final *"WHY?"*** in the poem. Cue them by holding up the *why* card.

3. Challenge the students to **think of two more "why" questions.**

4. Sometimes poets make up words to make their poems even more interesting. **Help students find the "made-up" word in this poem** (*why-ence*).

5. Follow up with another poem full of questions, **"Dreamland" by Carole Boston Weatherford** (2nd Grade, Week 19, page 125).

KEYS
by **Joy Acey**

Jingle, jangle,
keys on a ring.
To the house,
the car,
or anything.

Jingle, jangle,
can you hear
the keys
sing?

Take 5!

1. **Have your keys handy and shake them** at the beginning of each stanza as you read the poem aloud.

2. In repeated readings, **shake your keys at the beginning of each stanza** to cue the students to say the line *Jingle, jangle* each time.

3. For discussion: *Keys are for houses and cars and what else?*

4. We sometimes use one word to describe making a sound (such as *bark*) and another word to describe the sound itself (*woof*). **Think of things that you could describe as making a jingle/jangle noise** (keys, dog tags, spurs, bells).

5. Follow up with another poem about a jingly thing, **"Music Lesson" by Laura Purdie Salas** (2nd Grade, Week 25, page 131).

HOW MANY SLAMS ARE IN AN OLD SCREEN DOOR?
by **Allan Wolf**

How many slams
are in an old screen door?

One,
  two,
    three,
      four?

A hundred?

  A thousand?

A million?

  More?

How many slams
are in an old screen door?

Take 5!

1. Before reading this poem aloud, challenge students to **listen for number words** in the poem (*one, two, three, four, hundred, thousand, million*).

2. In the next read-aloud, **invite the students to say the lines for the number words**, *One, / two, / three, / four?* Cue them by holding up the corresponding fingers.

3. For discussion: ***How many times would you guess the classroom door opens in one hour?*** Try counting them.

4. Poets give their poems shape in many ways. This poem begins and ends with the same stanza; in between, the poem uses number words. **Invite students to echo read** the first and last stanzas as you read the poem aloud again.

5. Follow up with another poem about doors, **"How to Open the Attic Door" by April Halprin Wayland** (5th Grade, Week 26, page 252), or share Shel Silverstein's "How Many, How Much" from *A Light in the Attic*.

ANIMAL TALK
by **Charles Ghigna**

Ducks quack
Doves coo
Dogs bark
Cows moo

Birds sing
Bears growl
Bees buzz
Wolves howl

Geese honk
Gulls cry
Cats mew
Guess why

Mice squeak
Mules bray
Animals have
Something to say!

Take 5!

1. As you read this poem aloud, **make the animal sound** that corresponds to each line (*quack, coo, bark, moo,* etc.).

2. In a repeated reading, **invite students to make the animal sound** you have modeled after you read each line.

3. For discussion: ***What other sounds do animals make?*** Invite students to share examples from other languages. For instance, in English, roosters might crow *cock-a-doodle doo,* but in Spanish, roosters might *cantar* the sound *ki ki ri kí.*

4. Sometimes poets use words that mimic sounds, which is called *onomatopoeia.* **Challenge the students to see how many sound words they can find in this poem** (such as *quack, coo, moo, buzz, mew*).

5. Revisit another animal poem, **"Petting Zoo" by Laura Purdie Salas** (Kindergarten, Week 4, page 30), or share a few of the 200 poems in the *National Geographic Book of Animal Poetry*, compiled by J. Patrick Lewis.

WEEK 28: BOOKS

THE BOOK

by **Stephanie Calmenson**

Hello, I am a book—
A real book.
I am made of paper.
I have a front cover,
A back cover,
And pages in between
Filled with amazing surprises.
Ta-daa! Aren't I gorgeous?

Wait! Don't open me!
Not yet!
Not until you read
this WARNING:
Once you read a book,
you will want to read
another and another
and another.

Okay, you've been warned.
Are you ready?
Go ahead.
Open me.

Take 5!

1. **Select an additional book to read aloud later,** and open it dramatically as you get to the final line in reading this poem aloud.

2. Read the poem aloud again and **invite students to say the final line** (*Open me*) together. Read each line of the final stanza extra slowly, for dramatic effect.

3. For discussion: *What is your favorite book (so far)?*

4. **Discuss with students how many poems rhyme, but not all.** This poem is an example of *free verse.* It's also told from a unique point of view. Ask students who is "talking" in the poem (the book). Read/say the poem aloud together again.

5. For another poem about opening a book, read **"First" by Greg Pincus** (1st Grade, Week 28, page 94), or select a poem from *I Am the Book,* edited by Lee Bennett Hopkins.

POEMS ARE OUT OF THIS WORLD
by **Charles Ghigna**

Poems are stars
closer than Mars
waiting for you to explore.

Ready-set,
jump in your jet,
blow open the poetry door.

Take the dare,
fly through the air,
your rocket is ready to climb.

Go free and go far
toward your poetry star
on wings of rhythm and rhyme!

Take 5!

1. **Show a cutout star shape or star sticker before reading the poem aloud.** If possible, provide one for each student, too.

2. Next, **invite students to echo read** the poem, repeating each line after you read it aloud.

3. For discussion: *If you could take a ride in a rocket, where would you like to go?* The sun, the moon, a star, or maybe a certain planet?

4. **In this poem, there are rhymes in each stanza** (*stars/ Mars; set/jet; dare/air; far/star*) as well as across the stanzas (*explore/door; climb/rhyme*). With student help, place a star cutout or sticker on each rhyming word while reading the poem aloud again.

5. Another poet takes us to Mars with **"I Might Go to Mars" by Juanita Havill** (2nd Grade, Week 28, page 134).

LOOSE TOOTH, WHOSE TOOTH?
by **Carole Boston Weatherford**

Loose tooth, whose tooth?
Bat's tooth, rat's tooth.
Loose tooth, whose tooth?
Snail's tooth, whale's tooth.
Loose tooth, whose tooth?
Aardvark's tooth, shark's tooth.
Loose tooth, whose tooth?
Shrew's tooth, gnu's tooth.
Loose tooth, whose tooth?
Gorilla's tooth, chinchilla's tooth.
Loose tooth, whose tooth?
Piranha's tooth, iguana's tooth.
Loose tooth, whose tooth?
Boar's tooth, your tooth.

Take 5!

1. Before reading the poem aloud, **survey students on how many of them have a loose tooth.**

2. Read the poem aloud again and this time **students can say the repeated line *Loose tooth, whose tooth?*** each time it occurs.

3. For discussion: ***Which of these animals are new to you?*** If possible, look up images of unfamiliar animals on the Internet.

4. Poems usually rhyme at the end of lines, but sometimes they rhyme in the middle too, which is called *internal rhyme*. **Challenge the students to find the pairs of words that rhyme** (*bat/rat; snail/whale; aardvark/shark*, etc.).

5. Revisit a previous list poem about animals, **"Animal Talk" by Charles Ghigna** (Kindergarten, Week 27, page 53).

CRAYONS
by **Ann Whitford Paul**

C rayons, rainbow bright and
R ocket shaped, wait to blast
A cross a sheet of paper.
Y ou'd better use them fast
O r someone else will color them into
N ubs, small useless waxy
S tubs.

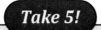

Take 5!

1. Hold and **show a handful of crayon pieces as you read this poem aloud.**

2. Share the poem aloud again and **invite students to say the first and last words of the poem** in unison while you read the rest.

3. For discussion: ***What is your favorite crayon color?***

4. Sometimes poets use each letter of a key word to begin each line of the poem, which is called *acrostic* poetry. **Highlight the first word of each line** to show how the letters of *crayons* were used.

5. For another example of an acrostic poem, share the baseball poem **"Last Try" by Avis Harley** (1st Grade, Week 31, page 97).

MY BIKE

by **Julie Larios**

My bike is like a silver shark
swimming in the sea—
as fast as a shark, as fierce as a shark,
and no one can ride it but me.

Take 5!

1. Before reading the poem aloud, **display an image of a bicycle and the image of a shark.**

2. Next, **invite students to echo read** the poem, repeating each line after you read it aloud. Break the third line into two parts for the echo reading.

3. **Encourage students to share a few bike stories** of their own.

4. Poets compare one thing to another to give us a fresh perspective on both things. **Lead the students in talking about how bikes and sharks are alike.** Use examples from the poem.

5. Share another riding poem with **"Rodeo" by Kristy Dempsey** (1st Grade, Week 3, page 69) or "Two Wheels That Go Around" by Michael Salinger, in *Gift Tag*, an e-book of holiday poems compiled by Vardell and Wong.

No Wonder
by **Constance Levy**

When rainstorms pound the ground
grasses shake and puddles sprout.
The weary earth grows woozy
from the battering about,
so no wonder when it's over
seasick worms come stumbling out.

Take 5!

1. **Read this poem aloud while playing a soundtrack of rain sounds.** A good source is this storm track on SoundCloud.com: soundcloud.com/imissjamglue/sounds-of-nature-thunder-and.

2. **Read the poem aloud again, inviting students to create their own storm noises** by patting their laps (for thunder in the first two lines) then rubbing their palms together (for rain in the remaining lines).

3. For discussion: *What are some other signs of storms?*

4. This poem uses several words that begin with *w*. Poets use this technique, called *alliteration*, to add to the sound qualities of the poem. **See if students can identify each of those *w* words and talk about the meanings of possibly unfamiliar words** (*weary, woozy*).

5. Revisit another weather poem, **"Stormy Day" by Rebecca Kai Dotlich** (Kindergarten, Week 17, page 43).

BOUNCING ALONG
by **Kristy Dempsey**

Crackety, Crickety, Clickety, Clack
The train rumbles over the rickety track.
It shakes and it quivers.
It bounces and jolts.
The rails jump and jiggle.
Please tighten the bolts!

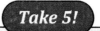

Take 5!

1. **Add energy to reading this poem aloud by incorporating motions for key words** like *shake, quiver, bounce, jolt, jump,* and *jiggle.*

2. **Invite students to echo read** only the words of the first line of the poem, repeating one word at a time after you read each word aloud.

3. For discussion: *If trains make a* **crackety, crickety, clickety, clack** *noise, what noises do cars make?* Bikes? Skates? Have fun experimenting with onomatopoeia and phonics!

4. Poets sometimes use groups of words that start with the same sound or letter, which is called *alliteration.* **Challenge the students to identify groups of words that start with the same letters** (e.g., *cr, cl, j*).

5. Connect this poem with another poem about transportation, **"Pick-Up Truck"** by Janet Wong (2nd Grade, Week 34, page 140).

Take 5!

1. Before sharing the poem, pack a small suitcase stuffed with funny vacation "necessities" to **unpack while reading the poem aloud**. Or just empty things out of a purse or backpack while performing the poem.

2. **Read the poem aloud together, challenging students to echo read** the poem, repeating each of the four stanzas after you read each one aloud.

3. For discussion: ***When you pack for a trip, what do you hate to leave behind?***

4. Students may need help knowing what a *centipede* is. **Look it up, show images, and talk about the rhyming pair** of *centipede* and *need* and how the rhyme depends on the final syllable of *centipede.*

5. For another poem about packing for a trip, check out **"By the Sea"** by Lesléa Newman (1st Grade, Week 35, page 101).

No Way!
by **David L. Harrison**

You mean
this dinky
bag
is it?

Half
my stuff
will
never fit.

Okay,
I'll leave
my
centipede

But all
this other
stuff
I need!

MOVING UP DAY
by **Janet Wong**

It's my last hour in K—
it's Moving Up Day!

And I know the way
down the hall to 1st grade.

The teachers are fun.
I've met every one!

Hip, hip, hooray:
it's Moving Up Day!

Take 5!

1. **Set the stage by donning a 1st-place ribbon or button** before reading the poem aloud.

2. In repeated readings, **invite students to say the line, *it's Moving Up Day!* each time it occurs.** Cue them with a cheering gesture or fist pump.

3. Invite students to share memories of **the first day of kindergarten.**

4. Each stanza in this poem includes an end-rhyme—even a "slant" rhyme or "almost" rhyme in *way* and *grade.* **Challenge the kids to identify each rhyming pair** (*K/Day; way/grade; fun/one; hooray/Day*). Share the whole poem aloud again.

5. Revisit the poem **"Kindergarten Kid" by Stephanie Calmenson** (Kindergarten, Week 2, page 28).

POEMS FOR FIRST GRADE

Common Core Standards
for First Grade (RL.1.4)

In sharing poetry with first graders, we help expand their growing knowledge of language, their joy in playing with words, and their emerging literacy.

We focus first on enjoyment and understanding, then guide students in understanding how poets express feelings in poetry and appeal to the senses through language.

We can also help students understand and identify the words and phrases poets use to communicate emotions and convey sensory experiences through poetry.

In fun and participatory ways, we can celebrate poetry while gently introducing and reinforcing key skills.

FIRST GRADE

week 1	School	Ready *by Joan Bransfield Graham*
week 2	More School	Underwear Scare *by Terry Webb Harshman*
week 3	Fun & Games	Rodeo *by Kristy Dempsey*
week 4	Pets	Fish *by Joy Acey*
week 5	More Pets	Litter's Littlest *by Avis Harley*
week 6	On the Ground	Tree I Leaned Against *by George Ella Lyon*
week 7	In the Water	Crocodile *by Ann Whitford Paul*
week 8	In the Air	Bat *by X.J. Kennedy*
week 9	Weather	My Dog *by Charles Waters*
week 10	Food	Snack Rules *by Robyn Hood Black*
week 11	More Food	Grandfather's Chopsticks *by Janet Wong*
week 12	House & Home	My Tree House *by Charles Ghigna*
week 13	Families	Abuelita *by Margarita Engle*
week 14	Community	Fire! *by Laura Purdie Salas*
week 15	Stuff We Love	Mud Supper *by Mary Quattlebaum*
week 16	Holidays	Photo Op *by Linda Sue Park*
week 17	Time Together	Watching Football *by Janet Wong*
week 18	Human Body	Baby Tooth *by Amy Ludwig VanDerwater*
week 19	More Human Body	Kerchoo! *by Cynthia Cotten*
week 20	Art & Colors	Clay Time *by Terry Webb Harshman*
week 21	Love & Friendship	Ingredients for a Valentine *by Bobbi Katz*
week 22	A Kinder Place	Embarrassed *by Jacqueline Jules*
week 23	Exploring	Antarctica, AntarcticO! *by Heidi Bee Roemer*
week 24	Science & Tech	Skype *by Janet Wong*
week 25	Song & Dance	Your Chance to Dance *by Brod Bagert*
week 26	Nonsense	Armadillo *by X.J. Kennedy*
week 27	World of Words	Gnat and Flea *by J. Patrick Lewis*
week 28	Books	First *by Greg Pincus*
week 29	Poetry Poems	A Poem a Day *by Stephanie Calmenson*
week 30	RR&R	Once a Week at Noon *by Jack Prelutsky*
week 31	Different Forms	Last Try *by Avis Harley*
week 32	Metaphor & Simile	See-Saw *by Graham Denton*
week 33	Personification	The Secret of the Clouds *by Allan Wolf*
week 34	On the Move	A Centipede's Excuse *by Kristy Dempsey*
week 35	Summer Vacation	By the Sea *by Lesléa Newman*
week 36	Looking Forward	Vacation *by Amy Ludwig VanDerwater*

*"One of my teachers told me, '**Never let a day go by without looking on three beautiful things**.' I try to live up to that and find it isn't difficult. The sky in all weathers is, for me, the first of these three things."*

David McCord

READY
by **Joan Bransfield Graham**

Just got a haircut,
   new sneakers
on my feet.
   Pencils, crayons,
backpack—my outfit
   is complete.
I'm headed
   for adventure . . .
new class, new desk—
   it's cool.
Let's cheer for
   all the newness
of the
   First
      Week of
        School!

Take 5!

1. Before reading this poem aloud, **hold up new school supplies** (like pencils, crayons, backpack) as your poetry prop to help focus on the poem topic.

2. Next, for a participatory reading, **invite students to join in on the last four words of the poem** (*First / Week of / School*) after you read the rest of the poem. Cue them to their reading by lifting your new school supplies prop.

3. For discussion: ***What are your favorite new school supplies?***

4. One of the key elements of many poems is rhyme. **Ask students to identify the ending rhymes** for this poem (*feet/ complete; cool/School*). Notice in one rhyming pair that the words may be of different syllable lengths.

5. Follow up with a related poem, **"Backpack" by Irene Latham** (5th Grade, Week 2, page 228), or a poem from *What a Day It Was at School!* by Jack Prelutsky.

UNDERWEAR SCARE
by **Terry Webb Harshman**

I got off the bus
and found my room.
I found my desk
   and chair.

Then suddenly
my teacher said,
"You're in your
   underwear!"

Down the hallway
I ran
   SCREAMING!

Thank goodness I
was only
   dreaming.

Take 5!

1. **Pantomime the motions suggested in the poem**: walk around the room, find a desk, sit in a chair, then run around the room and back to your desk.

2. Read the poem again with student participation, **inviting them to read the teacher's line** *You're in your/ underwear!* while you read the rest of the poem, pausing for extra drama before the final stanza.

3. **Encourage students to share funny things that could happen in dreams about school.**

4. Even beginning with the title of the poem, "Underwear Scare," the rhyming words are an important part of this poem. **Ask students to say the rhyming word in the second and fourth stanzas** (*underwear, dreaming*) as you read the poem aloud, stopping just short of completing those lines.

5. To follow up, share another poem about dreaming, **"Dreamland" by Carole Boston Weatherford** (2nd Grade, Week 19, page 125).

Take 5!

1. Prior to reading the poem, **set the stage by donning a cowboy hat** or bandana or tying a jump rope into a mock lasso. Slow down for the hyphenated words.

2. In repeated readings, **prepare students to join in on the final line,** *GO, Cowboy, GO!*

3. *Rodeo* is actually a Spanish word. **Share other Spanish words that are used by English speakers** (*coyote, armadillo, bronco, cafeteria*).

4. Sometimes poets like to use many words that start with the same sound (*alliteration*) to add to the sound of the poem. **Challenge students to identify a repeated sound at the beginning of words** in this poem (*b*). List and say the words that begin with this sound (*bucking, bronco, back-cracking, bare-backing*).

5. Another poem that describes a wild ride and also incorporates alliteration (featuring *s/sh*) is **"My Bike" by Julie Larios** (Kindergarten, Week 32, page 58), or share a selection from *Cowboys* by David L. Harrison.

RODEO
by **Kristy Dempsey**

I'm going to the rodeo,
a bucking bronco show,
a whip-snapping, back-cracking
bare-backing, nonstop action show,
this rodeo,
GO, Cowboy, GO!

FISH
by Joy Acey

What do fish do?
They swim in a bowl
by one or two.

What do fish eat?
Algae, slime
and fishbowl treats.

What do fish know
as they blow bubbles
in their bowl?

They know how to dive
and to race. Exploring spaces
in their fishbowl place.

Breathing in water
cool and blue.
That is more than
I can do.
How about you?

Take 5!

1. Sometimes poets like to ask questions in their poems. Point out that questions end in special punctuation: the question mark. Show a card or sign or image with a question mark on it and **invite students to listen for the questions** and look for the question marks in this poem as you read it aloud.

2. In a repeated reading, use the question mark card (from above) to cue students to **say the question lines aloud in unison**. Coach them on those lines beforehand, if needed.

3. For discussion: ***What can YOU do in the water?***

4. Repetition is a key building block in poetry. This poem repeats the use of questions. **Ask students to find where a question occurs** (the first lines of the first, second, and third stanzas plus the final line of the poem).

5. Follow up with another water-related poem, **"Tadpole Wishes" by Terry Webb Harshman** (Kindergarten, Week 7, page 33).

Take 5!

1. Explain the words *litter* (a group of newborn animals), *runt* (the smallest of the group), and *brood* (to worry about). **Alert students to listen for fun words** like *guzzle, nuzzle,* and *muzzle* as you read the poem aloud slowly.

2. **Invite students to join in on the phrase *guzzle and nuzzle my muzzle*.** Guess at the meanings of the words, and then look them up (*guzzle* = drink, *nuzzle* = cuddle, *muzzle* = mouth and nose).

3. For discussion: *Do you picture puppies or kittens (or some other animal)?*

4. **This poem is full of rhyme**—rhymes at the end of lines, at the end of stanzas, and even in the middle of lines (*internal rhyme*). Ask students to find examples. (Internal rhyme examples include *runt/bunch; speedy/greedy; nuzzle/muzzle.*)

5. Follow up by sharing **"Dog Walking Tanka" by Margarita Engle** (2nd Grade, Week 31, page 137) or **"All Worn Out" by Kristy Dempsey** (2nd Grade, Week 5, page 111).

LITTER'S LITTLEST
by **Avis Harley**

I'm the runt of the litter
and I'm feeling quite bitter
for I'm always shoved aside.

My siblings are stronger
with legs much longer
and their paws are pushy and wide.

They're extremely rude
at the Fountain of Food
and none of them brood on the needy.

I'm the runt of the bunch
and I'm missing my lunch
in the speedy stampede of the greedy.

But wait!! Here I find
human hands which are kind
airlifting me swiftly in place.

And now I can guzzle
and nuzzle my muzzle
all warm in my mother's embrace.

TREE I LEANED AGAINST
by **George Ella Lyon**

Tree I leaned against
looking for my elephant:
now you are moving!

Take 5!

1. **Read this poem aloud extra slowly while leaning against a hard surface.** Pause for extra drama before the final line.

2. For a follow-up reading, **invite students to say the last line in unison** after you read the rest of the poem.

3. For discussion: *Did you ever mistake one thing for another?* Maybe a snake for a garden hose, or a bug for a leaf?

4. Many poems rhyme, but not all. **This is an example of a poem form that usually does not rhyme, a haiku poem.** Originally a Japanese form of poetry, a haiku focuses on nature in only three lines (generally 5 syllables, 7 syllables, 5 syllables). Guide students in understanding the haiku form with this example.

5. Share another haiku, **"Waiting" by Lorie Ann Grover** (Kindergarten, Week 20, page 46).

CROCODILE
by **Ann Whitford Paul**

Crocodile
bares her teeth,
in a ravenous smile.
Her scaly tail
churns and splashes,
leaving a trail,
a liquid wake,
that ripples the surface,
ruffles the lake.
Her bubbled poem
sinks down low.
The fish read
        the foam,
            the froth,
and know
It's time to GO!

Take 5!

1. Feeling dramatic? **Read this poem as if you were a crocodile.** Slink around the room, bare your teeth, extend your arm as a tail, sink down low, pantomiming the descriptions in this poem. Then discuss possibly unfamiliar words: *ravenous, churn, liquid wake, surface, ruffles the lake, froth.*

2. Read the poem aloud again, and this time **invite the students to say the final line,** *It's time to GO!*

3. For discussion: **What animals might fear the crocodile?**

4. In this poem, the poet uses alliteration to repeat the same sound at the beginning of several words for greater emphasis. **Help students locate examples of this** (e.g., *f* in *fish, foam, froth*).

5. Contrast this poem with **"Crocodile" by Deborah Chandra** (4th Grade, Week 32, page 218).

BAT

by **X.J. Kennedy**

One day a bat
Got into my room.
My mother went SWAT
With a big fat broom

And drove it to
The window sill.
It flew outside.
I miss it still.

It must be hard
To be a bat
Hanging all night
Head down like that.

You'd think he'd get
A runny nose,
Hanging on tight
With ten tense toes.

Take 5!

1. To set the stage before reading this poem aloud, **make an origami bat.** A simple model is available at nickrobinson.info/origami/diagrams/bat.htm. After reading the poem aloud, hang the bat upside down.

2. **Invite students to echo read each line** of the poem after you read it. Slow down to read each word in the final line with extra emphasis.

3. For discussion: *Have you had unexpected animal visitors in your home?*

4. Poets often call upon the senses to make their poems more powerful. **Encourage students to identify words and phrases from the poem that suggest sights and sounds.** An example might include the *SWAT* sound of the broom.

5. Follow up by reading aloud another poem about a bat, **"My Pet" by David L. Harrison** (2nd Grade, Week 4, page 110).

Take 5!

1. Before reading the poem aloud, **make a list of dog names** based on students' pets or pets they wish they had. Add *Fido* to the list to introduce the dog in this poem. Pause dramatically at the end of each line in this poem.

2. In repeated readings, **invite students to read the second line of each stanza** except the first stanza (*It hails; It snows; It sleets; Rainbows*).

3. For discussion: *What might happen when Fido is sleeping?*

4. Here the poet uses key words to match emotions to weather events. **Review weather words** such as *hail, snow, sleet, rainbow*.

5. Look for **"My Dog Jack Thinks Up His Valentine" by Patricia Hubbell** (2nd Grade, Week 21, page 127), or selections from *Stella, Unleashed* by Linda Ashman.

MY DOG
by **Charles Waters**

My dog controls
The weather.

When Fido barks
It hails,

When Fido's quiet
It snows,

When Fido's angry
It sleets,

When Fido's happy . . .
R a i n b o w s.

SNACK RULES
by **Robyn Hood Black**

Don't talk with your mouth full—
full of peanut butter.
Anything you try to say
wll cmmm out as a mmmttrr.

Take 5!

1. **Read this short poem aloud with exaggerated slowness** and facial expressions, especially on the last line.

2. Read the poem aloud again, but this time **invite students to repeat each line after you**, including mumbling the final line.

3. For discussion: *What are your favorite snacks?*

4. **Sometimes poets break the rules and make up words** that fit the poem or add an unusual twist. In this poem, the poet misspells three of the words in the last line on purpose (*wll, cmmm, mmmttrr*). Why? Guide students in a discussion of this choice and its effect. Write the words correctly (*will come out as a mutter*) for contrast.

5. Share another poem about food, snacks, and peanut butter with **"Sack Lunch" by Charles Waters** (Kindergarten, Week 11, page 37).

GRANDFATHER'S CHOPSTICKS
by **Janet Wong**

Take 5!

1. If possible, **demonstrate how chopsticks work and gesture with them** as you read this poem aloud. If necessary, two long pencils or drinking straws can substitute.

2. The title line appears twice in the poem (beginning the first and third stanzas). **Invite students to say the title line each time it appears** as you read the rest of the poem aloud.

3. For discussion: *What are some foods you especially enjoy eating* with a grandparent or other favorite family member?

4. Appealing to the senses is a key element in poetry. The sense of taste is very vivid in this poem. **Lead students in a discussion of how the poet uses sensory details,** sharing words from the poem as examples (*slippery noodles, crispy skin*).

5. Compare this poem with another food-related poem by the same poet, **"The Breakfast Boss" by Janet Wong** (3rd Grade, Week 13, page 159).

Grandfather's chopsticks
are like extra-long
superhero fingers,
able to grab anything
on the big round
restaurant table.

He picks up
a piece of my favorite
honey walnut shrimp
and puts it on my plate.
Slippery noodles.
Fried chicken—
crispy skin
and tender white meat.

Grandfather's chopsticks
are pretty smart:
how do they know
exactly
what I want to eat?

MY TREE HOUSE
by **Charles Ghigna**

Welcome to my tree house,
my free house,
my *me* house,

where I come to ponder,
to wonder,
to look up at the sky,

where I come to daydream,
to play dream,
to watch the clouds roll by,

where the air is fresher,
no pressure,
where treetops swish and sway,

where I come to look at
the books that
take me far away.

Take 5!

1. Before sharing this poem, take a moment to **encourage students to close their eyes and imagine** a big leafy tree, a ladder up high, and a tree house. Then continue by reading this poem aloud.

2. Next, **invite students to join you in reading aloud the first stanza.** If necessary, write the words *tree, free, me* on cards to cue students to the order of these words in reading the stanza.

3. For discussion: *If you could have a tree house, what would it be like?*

4. Sometimes poets arrange their words into groups called *stanzas*. This poem contains five stanzas. A stanza can have any number of lines. **Help students see that this poem is made up of *tercets*** (three-line stanzas).

5. Follow up with **"The Front Yard Where the Maple Tree Stands" by Allan Wolf** (4th Grade, Week 12, page 198).

ABUELITA
by **Margarita Engle**

We called her little grandmother
even though she was big.

Her house was small
and the street was muddy.
Her neighbors rode horses
and lived in thatched huts.
She believed in the goodness
of ladylike manners.
She taught me how to embroider
a garden,
decorating the world
with a sharp needle,
one flowery stitch
at a time.

Take 5!

1. Before reading the poem aloud, **talk about the different words we use for *grandmother*,** such as *abuelita, oma, nana,* and so on.

2. Invite students to set the stage by **reading the first two lines aloud together while you read the rest** aloud slowly. Display the poem so students can read their lines, or invite them to echo you.

3. Invite students to **share memories or feelings about their own grandmothers**.

4. Sometimes poems rhyme and sometimes they don't. In this case, the poem doesn't rhyme but still has a rhythm that emerges through the length of the lines. **Challenge students to point out lines that "go together" and have a similar rhythm** even though they don't end in a rhyme (e.g., *Her neighbors rode horses / and lived in thatched huts*).

5. Pair this poem with **"Doña Pepita" by Guadalupe Garcia McCall** (5th Grade, Week 14, page 240).

FIRE!
by Laura Purdie Salas

Sirens—
Flashing red blur
speeding to gritty smoke
Jackets, ladders, hoses, helmets:
Heroes!

Take 5!

1. This short, succinct poem provides an ideal moment to **remind students about fire safety procedures** for the classroom and school. Then read it aloud slowly and with special emphasis on the first and last words.

2. In repeated readings, **divide students into two groups to read the poem in alternating lines** (line 1 = group 1; line 2 = group 2, etc.). They can also alternate reading the four words in line 4 for greater impact. Practice, then read it again several times.

3. **Talk about the proper use of the 911 emergency phone line.**

4. There are many special forms of poems that poets like to try. **This poem is written in the form of a *cinquain*,** a five-line poem with one topic. Discuss the details the poet provides about actions (*flashing, speeding*) and feelings (*Heroes*) in this poem.

5. Share another poem about firefighters, **"Fire Station" by Sara Holbrook** (2nd Grade, Week 14, page 120).

MUD SUPPER
by **Mary Quattlebaum**

Mud supper, mud supper,
What can I make?
Mud fries, mud pies,
Mud-frosted cake.

Mud beans, mud greens,
Mud ham and cheese.
I'll give you a taste,
If you say please.

Mud supper, mud supper,
So much to eat.
Mud-luscious, mud-licious,
Mud-yummy treat!

Take 5!

1. If you're feeling brave, you can **sing this poem to the tune of "On Top of Old Smoky."** Or read it aloud emphasizing the word *mud* each time it occurs.

2. **Invite students to join in on the word *mud*** in the poem as you read the poem aloud again. Display the poem and/or hold up a word card with *mud* on it as a cue.

3. For discussion: *What else can you make out of mud?*

4. Poems usually rhyme at the end of lines, but sometimes they rhyme in the middle, too, which is called *internal rhyme*. **Challenge the students to find the pairs of words that rhyme** at the end of lines (*make/cake; cheese/please; eat/treat*) and in the middle (*fries/pies; beans/greens*).

5. Contrast making food out of mud with baking real cookies with **Joan Bransfield Graham's poem, "Who Invented Cookies?"** (Kindergarten, Week 10, page 36).

PHOTO OP
by Linda Sue Park

"Get together, look this way,
Lean in—you'll have to squeeze.
That's it—that's good, just stay right there.
And one-two-three—say CHEESE!"

Can someone tell me why it is
we have to holler "cheese"?
Just once I'd like a photo snapped
while everyone yells "FLEAS!"

Take 5!

1. **Pose the class together for an informal group photograph** taken with your camera, phone, or iPad. Read this poem aloud before you snap the photo. Say *fleas!*

2. **Invite the students to join in on saying *CHEESE!* and *FLEAS!*** Alert them to the poet's use of all capital letters for greater emphasis and a cue to their reading.

3. For discussion: ***What makes a school or family photo funny?***

4. **The poet uses capital letters to indicate when words should receive greater emphasis** (*CHEESE!, FLEAS!*). Guide the students in discussing this choice and contrast it with the impact of the words in lower case (*cheese, fleas*).

5. Another occasion that often calls for photos is a choir performance such as the one depicted in **"My Kindergarten Choir" by Avis Harley** (Kindergarten, Week 16, page 42).

WATCHING FOOTBALL
by **Janet Wong**

Dad and my older brother
are slouching on the couch,
each with his own bag
of potato chips.
I squeeze in between them.
They say
they're busy
watching football
but what they're really doing
is eating potato chips.
I reach into both their bags
at the same time
that the green guy
catches the ball.
Touchdown!
I pump two fists full of chips
in the air
and holler, *Woohoo!*
Why aren't they cheering,
too?

(Oops—wrong team.)

Take 5!

1. Read this poem aloud and **pantomime gestures and actions that fit the poem** (slouching, reaching, pumping fists, cheering).

2. In repeated readings, invite students to **cheer the words *Touchdown!* and *Woohoo!*** Display the words of the poem, if possible, and cue students with two raised arms for *Touchdown!* and one for *Woohoo!*

3. For discussion: ***Do you like watching sports or playing sports better?***

4. Many poems evoke strong feelings and emotions as we hear them or read them. **Discuss with students how this poem captures both excitement and embarrassment** and guide them in pinpointing which words and phrases communicate which feeling.

5. Follow up with **"Running Back" by Jacqueline Jules** (4th Grade, Week 3, page 189).

BABY TOOTH
by Amy Ludwig VanDerwater

One wiggly week.
One apple bite.
One twist.
One pull.
I won the fight.

My face is full
of first grade style.

My tongue
peeks out
a window
in the middle
of my smile.

Take 5!

1. As you read this poem aloud, **pretend you have a loose tooth** and pantomime the actions suggested in the poem (bite apple, twist tooth, pull tooth, peek out tongue, smile).

2. The word *one* is repeated several times in this poem. That's the perfect way to invite students to participate in another oral reading. **Raise one finger to cue students when they should join in on saying *one* each time it occurs** in the first stanza.

3. For discussion: *What is the best way to lose a loose tooth?*

4. Repetition is a key ingredient in creating poems. Sometimes a poet uses repetition not just to enhance the sound of the poem, but to emphasize meaning. **Lead the students in discussing how the poet repeats the word *one* in every line of the first stanza, including the homonym *won*.**

5. Combine this poem with **"Tooth,"** also by **Amy Ludwig VanDerwater** (Kindergarten, Week 18, page 44).

KERCHOO!
by **Cynthia Cotten**

Mary Kate began to sneeze.
She held her breath to make it stop.
The sneezes all piled up inside,
until at last her head went "pop!"

Take 5!

1. **Read this poem aloud accompanied by exaggerated expressions** and gestures (take a breath, hold your nose, hold your breath, gasp a pop) that suit the lines of the poem.

2. Students can **join in on the final word** *pop* as you read the poem aloud again.

3. For discussion: ***How can you stop a sneeze?***

4. Sometimes poets use words that mimic sounds, which is called *onomatopoeia*. Challenge the students to **identify the sound words** in this poem (*pop* and the title, *Kerchoo*). Then read the poem (including title) aloud together again.

5. Follow this poem about a sneeze with another about a yawn, **"Catching a Yawn" by Avis Harley** (3rd Grade, Week 18, page 164).

CLAY TIME
by Terry Webb Harshman

Hooray! Hooray!
Today's the day
I get to make a *thing* of clay!

I rolled that cool, gray lump about,
Until a PONY galloped out!

Take 5!

1. If available, **roll a ball of clay, Play-doh, or putty in your hands while reading this poem aloud.**

2. For a choral reading, **coach the students to say the word *PONY*** when it occurs in the poem. Read the poem aloud again and pause dramatically before cuing students for their word.

3. For discussion: *What kinds of things are made of clay* (e.g., dishes, bricks flower pots)?

4. **Sometimes poets use basic graphic elements** to add interest to their poems, such as italics, capital letters, and even punctuation like exclamation marks. Guide students in discussing how these three components in this poem (*thing, PONY, exclamation marks*) help show us how to read the poem. Then read the poem aloud together again.

5. Connect this poem to one about mud by revisiting **"Mud Supper" by Mary Quattlebaum** (1st Grade, Week 15, page 81).

INGREDIENTS FOR A VALENTINE
by **Bobbi Katz**

Red velvet ribbon
White paper lace
The shape of a heart
that you can trace
A friend to send a valentine
Some special words:
WILL YOU BE MINE?

Take 5!

1. Before reading this poem aloud, **hold up a valentine card** or red paper cut-out heart and ask students to guess what this poem is about.

2. Invite students to echo read the poem, repeating each line after you read it aloud. **Everyone can trace the shape of a heart in the air while reading lines 3 and 4.**

3. For discussion: *What makes a friend special?*

4. **Invite students to tap the rhythm of the poem** as you share it aloud again. Like a composer with the notes of a song, poets give their poems a beat, too.

5. Share another poem about friendship,r **"The Do Kind" by Janet Wong** (3rd Grade, Week 21, page 167).

EMBARRASSED
by **Jacqueline Jules**

Why did I say that?
What's wrong with my brain?
Words spilled like soda,
and now there's a stain.

Sometimes, I'm so sloppy,
words fly everywhere,
sort of like potato chips
that end up in your hair.

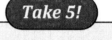

Take 5!

1. Before reading this poem in a soft voice, ask students to think about this question while they listen to the poem: *Have you ever said something and wished you could take it back?*

2. Next, **divide the students into two groups—one to say the first line and one to say the second line.** Display the poem and read it aloud again.

3. For discussion: *How do you make it right when you've said something wrong?*

4. In this poem, the poet explores emotions by asking questions and making comparisons. Guide students in exploring how details help us understand how the poet feels in this poem. **How do we feel when we make a real mess OR a mess with our words?**

5. The perfect companion poem for this one is **"Something I Did" by Janet Wong** (Kindergarten, Week 22, page 48).

Take 5!

1. **Read this poem aloud in a shivery voice while pantomiming being very, very cold** (shaking, stomping, feeling your ears and nose).

2. Read the poem again and **invite students to raise their hands whenever you say a word with a long o sound** in it. And there are many (13)! This offers a perfect phonics-poetry connection.

3. For discussion: *What are the best and worst things about cold days?*

4. The repeated sound of *o* is the key building block for this poem. Lead the students in making a list of all the words from the poem that have a long *o* sound. Note that the sound may be spelled in a variety of ways (*o, ow, oe*). **Using a repeated vowel sound like this is a fancy poetic technique called *assonance*!**

5. For another poem about being cold, look for **"After Sledding" by Betsy Franco** (2nd Grade, Week 17, page 123).

ANTARCTICA, ANTARCTIC*O*!
by **Heidi Bee Roemer**

I'm c*O*ld as a Sn*O*w K*O*ne;
my t*O*es are like lead.
My ears? They're both fr*O*zen,
My n*O*se? R*O*sy red.

As p*O*lar winds bl*O*w,
I'm chilled to the b*O*ne.
The thermometer tells me
what I should have kn*O*wn—

It's zer*O* degrees!
. . . I wish I'd stayed h*O*me.

SKYPE

by **Janet Wong**

Once a month
we Skype with Dad
who's in the army.
I'm so glad
that he can tell
how tall I've grown.
You can't see
on our telephone—
but here
with our computer screen
he knows exactly
what we mean
when Mom says
I'm a big kid now.
His eyes glow
when he says,
"I'm proud."

Take 5!

1. This is a poem that lends itself perfectly to sharing with a principal, parent, or another class via Skype, cell phone, or other means. Ideally, you could **get a volunteer adult to read the poem aloud to your class via Skype!**

2. For a choral reading, **coach the students to say the final line, "I'm proud."** Read the poem aloud again and pause for their unison line.

3. For discussion: *How do you keep in touch with family or friends who are far away?*

4. In this poem, we see a little bit about the feelings of all three people in the poem. **Guide the students in finding the key words or lines that communicate the emotions of the child** (*I'm so glad*), the Mom (*says / I'm a big kid now*), and the Dad (*His eyes glow / "I'm proud."*).

5. For another poem about keeping in touch by using technology, look for **"Vacation Communication" by Carol-Ann Hoyte** (3rd Grade, Week 24, page 170).

YOUR CHANCE TO DANCE
by **Brod Bagert**

Don't just stand there in a trance.
Dance! Dance! Dance! Dance!
You can do it. Take a chance.
Dance! Dance! Dance! Dance!

Feel the rhythm in advance . . .
Lift your head and take a stance . . .
Give the room a final glance . . .
And . . .

    Dance! Dance! **Dance!** Dance!

    Dance! Dance!

Dance!

Take 5!

1. Feeling brave? **Try dancing while reading this poem aloud.** Simply take one step forward or backward each time you say the word *dance,* alternating forward and backward.

2. Read the poem again, and this time **invite students to say the word** *dance* each time it occurs, and to step-dance with you while you read aloud.

3. For discussion: *What makes you want to dance?*

4. Rhythm is a key component in dancing and often in poetry, too. **Here the poet repeats the word** *dance* to give the poem a strong rhythm, but also ends every line in a word that rhymes with *dance.* Lead students in identifying each of those rhyming words (*trance, chance, advance, stance, glance*).

5. Share another rhythmic, dance-inspired poem with **"Beats on Top of Your Head"** by Jaime Adoff (5th Grade, Week 25, page 251).

ARMADILLO
by X.J. Kennedy

The armadillo dwells inside
The scaly armor of his hide
And while deep down he's soft and sweet,
He's harder than a city street.
So please don't pick an armadillo
To go to sleep on. Use your pillow.

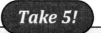

Take 5!

1. Before reading this poem aloud, show an image of an armadillo. **Ask students to guess what this poem is about** and to share what they know about this animal.

2. Part of the fun of this poem is the surprise ending. **Invite students to say the last three words in the final line** (*Use your pillow*) while you read the rest aloud.

3. For discussion: ***What other animals might be hard on the outside but soft on the inside*** (*e.g., turtle, crab, snail*)?

4. This poem uses several words that begin with the *s* sound. **Guide students in identifying each of those *s* words** (such as *soft, sweet, city, street*), noting that sometimes the *s* sound is spelled with a soft *c*. Poets use this technique of *alliteration* to add to the sound qualities of the poem.

5. For another poem that also includes a *pillow* and an *armadillo*, share **"A Plague of Penguins" by Julie Larios** (3rd Grade, Week 4, page 150).

GNAT AND FLEA
by J. Patrick Lewis

If it jumps, it's a *flea*,
If it flies, it's a *gnat*.
A *gnat* has wings,
I am certain of that.
A bunch of fleas—a swarm,
A batch of gnats—a cloud,
A bunch of dogs
With munchy fleas
Cries out loud.

Take 5!

1. Read this poem aloud **using a high-pitched voice for the lines related to fleas** (lines 1, 5), a low-pitched voice for the lines about gnats (lines 2, 3, 4, 6), and a normal voice for the lines about dogs (lines 7, 8, 9). You may need to alert students to the silent *g* in *gnat*.

2. Then invite students to jump during the flea lines, make flying motions during the gnat lines, and make scratching motions during the dog lines while you read the whole poem aloud. **Use your voice (high, low, normal) to cue students to the correct motions.** Read and perform it several times to get it all right!

3. For discussion: *Which is more annoying, a gnat or a flea?*

4. Sometimes poets weave facts into their poems. Use this poem to **discuss collective names for groups of animals.**

5. For another poem by **J. Patrick Lewis** that compares two animals, read **"Frog and Toad"** (Kindergarten, Week 21, page 47), or look for more insect poems in *Hey There, Stink Bug!* by Leslie Bulion.

FIRST
by **Greg Pincus**

First there was this poem.
Next there was this book.
And they were both quite lonely
Until you took a look.

Take 5!

1. Feeling bold? You can **sing this poem to the tune of "The Farmer in the Dell."**

2. If you prefer, you can simply read the poem aloud and invite students to echo read each line as you read it. Or you might teach students the song, or **display the words of the poem and sing the poem together.**

3. For discussion: *What is your favorite book (so far)?*

4. Sometimes poets use their imaginations to guess what it might be like if something that is not alive had a real personality. This technique is called *personification.* **Guide the students in determining which words or lines in this poem suggest *this poem* and *this book* have human feelings** (*And they were both quite lonely*).

5. Follow up with another poem about books from the point of view of a book, **"The Book" by Stephanie Calmenson** (Kindergarten, Week 28, page 54).

A POEM A DAY
by **Stephanie Calmenson**

A poem a day
keeps the blues away.
Write one.
Read one.
Do you really
need one?
Yes!
A poem a day
keeps the blues away.

Take 5!

1. As you read this poem aloud, **snap your fingers or clap your hands.** Pause before the word *Yes!* and linger on it, dragging out the *s* sound.

2. Read the poem aloud again. **Invite students to say the repeated refrain** (the first two lines and the last two lines) and the word *Yes!* while you read the rest.

3. For discussion: *What else do you like to do to* keep the blues away?

4. Poets give their poems shape in many ways. Repeating key words or lines helps build a poem and can add to the distinctive rhythm. **Guide students in discussing how the poet uses repetition in the beginning and ending of the poem.**

5. Follow up with another poem about poetry that incorporates repetition, **"Poem Like the Sea" by Patricia Hubbell** (3rd Grade, Week 29, page175).

ONCE A WEEK AT NOON
by **Jack Prelutsky**

Once a week at noon,
I eat a neon sign
Without a fork or spoon—
Light lunches are divine.

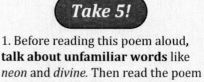

Take 5!

1. Before reading this poem aloud, **talk about unfamiliar words** like *neon* and *divine.* Then read the poem aloud with a fork and spoon in hand, if available.

2. Invite students to echo read the poem, repeating each line after you read it aloud. **Talk about the pun in the final line:** *light lunches* could mean eating a small amount of food or eating a lunch made of a neon light—which is absurd, of course.

3. For discussion: ***What can you really eat without a fork or spoon?***

4. Many of Prelutsky's poems have a regular beat that can be set to music or sung. **Display the words of the poem and try leading the students in singing the poem** to the tune of "Row, Row, Row Your Boat."

5. Share another sing-able poem by **Jack Prelutsky, "The World's Most Ancient Ant"** (Kindergarten, Week 6, page 32). This one can be sung to the tune of "99 Bottles of Pop."

LAST TRY
by **Avis Harley**

BALL THREEEE!
Adrenaline high.
STEEE-RIIIKE TWO!!
Empty sky.
Bases loaded
And one
Last try:
Life—in the bat of an eye.

Take 5!

1. **Read each line of this poem aloud slowly while pantomiming** the movements suggested in the poem (swinging a bat, looking in the sky). If possible, include a baseball bat.

2. For a choral reading, **coach the students in saying line 3, *STEEE-RIIIKE TWO!!*** with gusto. Read the poem aloud again and pause for their unison line.

3. For discussion: *What is the best thing about a baseball or softball game?*

4. Sometimes poets use each letter of a key word to begin each line of a poem, which is called *acrostic poetry*. **Highlight the first word of each line to show how the letters of *BASEBALL* are used.**

5. Share two other acrostic poems as examples of this poem form: **"Crayons" by Ann Whitford Paul** (Kindergarten, Week 31, page 57) or **"Music Lesson" by Laura Purdie Salas** (2nd Grade, Week 25, page 131).

SEE-SAW
by **Graham Denton**

life without a friend
is a see-saw with no one
on the other end

Take 5!

1. Before reading the poem aloud, **talk about the word** *see-saw*, a popular piece of playground equipment. If necessary, demonstrate the basics of a see-saw with a ruler and a can or jar for the middle support.

2. **Read the poem aloud again, inviting students to say the word** *see-saw* in the middle of the poem. They can stand up while saying *see*, then sit down while saying *saw*.

3. For discussion: ***When do you miss a friend most?***

4. This is another **example of a haiku poem** (containing three lines with generally 5 syllables, 7 syllables, 5 syllables). Usually haiku do not rhyme; however, this haiku does indeed include a rhyming pair of words. Lead students in identifying the beats in each line and the rhyming words (*friend, end*).

5. To follow up with another haiku poem, revisit **"Tree I Leaned Against" by George Ella Lyon** (1st Grade, Week 6, page 72), or selections from *Guyku: A Year of Haiku for Boys* by Bob Raczka.

Take 5!

1. If a window is nearby, **take a few moments for some cloud watching** prior to reading this poem aloud. Or check out CloudAppreciationSociety.org for cloud images.

2. For a repeated reading, **invite students to echo read each line of the poem**, repeating after you read each line aloud.

3. For discussion: *What do you see in the clouds?*

4. This poet gives human qualities to something that is not human, which is called *personification*. **Guide the students in identifying the key words or lines in this poem that humanize clouds** (*that cloud above me wore a pair / of fluffy cotton thunder-wear!*).

5. Revisit and reread another underwear poem, **"Underwear Scare" by Terry Webb Harshman** (1st Grade, Week 2, page 68).

THE SECRET OF THE CLOUDS
by **Allan Wolf**

I saw up in the sky, by chance,
a cloud who wasn't wearing pants.
And I discovered then and there
that cloud above me wore a pair
of fluffy cotton thunder-wear!

A CENTIPEDE'S EXCUSE
by Kristy Dempsey

I'm running late, no time to wait,
I cannot find my shoe.
I'm late for school, a broken rule,
detention makes me blue.
I found one underneath my chair,
another on the seat.
I would have been on time for school
if I had just two feet!

Take 5!

1. Place two or more different shoes nearby, one under a chair. Then **read the poem aloud, acting as if you are hunting for each shoe.** You may need to explain the word *detention*.

2. Display the words of the poem and **ask for eight volunteers to help read the poem aloud**, one volunteer for each line of the poem. Students can stand in a row with legs extended, showing off their shoes as they read their lines aloud.

3. For discussion: *What makes you late sometimes?*

4. Guide students in identifying words that rhyme in this poem. In this case there are both end rhymes (*shoe/blue; seat/feet*) and internal rhymes (*late/wait; school/rule*). Read the poem out loud again, and **invite students to extend a shoe when they hear a rhyme.**

5. Share another poem that features feet, **"Tadpole Wishes" by Terry Webb Harshman** (Kindergarten, Week 7, page 33).

Take 5!

1. If possible, set the stage for this poem by **gathering a few of the items mentioned in the poem.** Pick the items up one at a time as you read the lines that refer to those objects, showing them to the students.

2. To follow up, **invite students to echo read** only the last two lines of the poem.

3. For discussion: *What is your favorite thing to do at the beach?*

4. Talk about how rhyming words help turn this list of beach items into a poem. Lead them in identifying some of the pairs of words that rhyme (*beach/peach; chips/dips; boat/float; towels/trowels*). Students who are really observant may also **notice the use of alliteration** (repeated initial consonants) with the repeated use of *s, fl, t, b,* and *k* sounds. Look for examples of these, too.

5. Follow up with another poem about packing all kinds of things for a getaway, **"Family Vacation" by Allan Wolf** (5th Grade, Week 35, page 261).

BY THE SEA
by **Lesléa Newman**

What a great day for the beach,
I think I'll bring along a peach,
An apple, orange and some chips,
Carrots, celery and some dips.
Sunscreen, sunhat and a boat,
Snorkles, flippers and a float.
Lounge chairs, ear plugs and three towels,
Beachballs, shovels, buckets, trowels.
Beach umbrellas and some lotion,
Wetsuits to wear in the ocean.
Bathing cap and tiny, teeny
Itsy bitsy blue bikini,
Kickboard, kayak and canoe,
Sandwiches for me and you.
Blankets, sand mats and some pails,
Frisbees and a raft with sails.
I think it would be much less fuss,
If the beach just came to us.

VACATION
by **Amy Ludwig VanDerwater**

You think
I'm here
but I'm inside
my mind

I travel
far and wide
from city park
to mountain peak

I may be gone
a week
(or two)

but you
won't know
where I go

hike
    bike
        train
            plane

when I vacation
in my brain.

Take 5!

1. Prior to reading the poem aloud, ask students to close their eyes and **imagine a summer trip to someplace wonderful.** Then read the poem aloud, slowly and quietly.

2. For repeated readings, **invite four volunteers to read one word aloud each—*hike, bike, train, plane.*** Read the rest of the poem aloud, pausing dramatically before the final two lines.

3. For discussion: *If you could imagine any vacation at all, what would it be like?*

4. Sometimes poems rhyme and sometimes they don't. **In this case, the poem doesn't have a regular rhyme, but it does have some rhyming words.** Challenge the students to point them out (*inside/wide; know/go; hike/bike; train/plane/brain*).

5. For another poem about traveling through our imaginations, share **"I Might Go to Mars" by Juanita Havill** (2nd Grade, Week 28, page 134).

POEMS FOR SECOND GRADE

COMMON CORE STANDARDS
FOR SECOND GRADE (RL.2.4)

In sharing poetry with second graders, we can support their expanding vocabularies, promote their playful engagement with words and language, and lead them in connecting the spoken and written word.

First we focus on enjoyment and understanding, then we guide students in responding to the rhythm of poetry and recognizing how rhyme is used in poems.

We can also explore how repetition and alliteration can help shape a poem and how meaning emerges.

In fun and participatory ways, we can celebrate poetry while gently introducing and reinforcing key skills.

SECOND GRADE

week 1	School	The Library *by Sara Holbrook*
week 2	More School	Recess *by Avis Harley*
week 3	Fun & Games	The Winner *by Georgia Heard*
week 4	Pets	My Pet *by David L. Harrison*
week 5	More Pets	All Worn Out *by Kristy Dempsey*
week 6	On the Ground	The Woodland Vole *by Ken Slesarik*
week 7	In the Water	The Star-Nosed Mole *by Leslie Bulion*
week 8	In the Air	How Big Is the Atlas Moth? *by Deborah Ruddell*
week 9	Weather	Why Does Weather? *by Mary Quattlebaum*
week 10	Food	Crunch *by Debbie Levy*
week 11	More Food	A Taste of Taco *by Rebecca Kai Dotlich*
week 12	House & Home	Backyard Swing *by X.J. Kennedy*
week 13	Families	Double the Trouble *by Janet Wong*
week 14	Community	Fire Station *by Sara Holbrook*
week 15	Stuff We Love	Bubble Gum *by Greg Pincus*
week 16	Holidays	Christmas Is *by George Ella Lyon*
week 17	Time Together	After Sledding *by Betsy Franco*
week 18	Human Body	Momma's Trying *by Janet Wong*
week 19	More Human Body	Dreamland *by Carole Boston Weatherford*
week 20	Art & Colors	Lizard and Chameleon *by J. Patrick Lewis*
week 21	Love & Friendship	My Dog Jack Thinks Up His Valentine *by Patricia Hubbell*
week 22	A Kinder Place	Forgive and Forget *by Janet Wong*
week 23	Exploring	Africa's Child *by Carole Boston Weatherford*
week 24	Science & Tech	Appy Birthday *by April Halprin Wayland*
week 25	Song & Dance	Music Lesson *by Laura Purdie Salas*
week 26	Nonsense	Half-Past Never *by Lesléa Newman*
week 27	World of Words	Spanish Ears *by Carmen T. Bernier-Grand*
week 28	Books	I Might Go to Mars *by Juanita Havill*
week 29	Poetry Poems	Recipe for a Poem *by Kristy Dempsey*
week 30	RR&R	Rough and Tumble *by Lesléa Newman*
week 31	Different Forms	Dog-Walking Tanka *by Margarita Engle*
week 32	Metaphor & Simile	Outer Spaceman *by Julie Larios*
week 33	Personification	My Carrots Are Angry *by Jack Prelutsky*
week 34	On the Move	Pick-Up Truck *by Janet Wong*
week 35	Summer Vacation	Summer Showers *by Carole Gerber*
week 36	Looking Forward	The Secret Seed *by Allan Wolf*

*"Poetry isn't trying to get us to do anything. It **is simply inviting us** to think, and feel, and see."*

◦๏๛ Naomi Shihab Nye ๛๏◦

Take 5!

1. Arrange a quick visit to the library or bring a pile, bin, or cart of library books on a variety of topics. **Show students your public library card and have applications available**. Then read this poem aloud. Slow down to enunciate each item in lines 5-16.

2. Read the poem aloud again, and **invite students to read the last three lines in unison.**

3. For discussion: *What is your favorite book you've read (so far)?*

4. Help students find the rhyming pairs of "words that sound alike." **Ask students: *What are the words that rhyme?*** (These include: *door/more; quakes/snakes; beans/machines; bats/cats; book/look/cook; poem/home; about/out.*) Read the poem aloud again, but pause before the second word in each rhyming pair and wait for the students to chime in with the correct response (*more, snakes, machines, cats, look, home, out*).

5. Look for **"Poems Are Out of This World!" by Charles Ghigna** (Kindergarten, Week 29, page 55), or a poem from *Please Bury Me in the Library* by J. Patrick Lewis.

THE LIBRARY
by **Sara Holbrook**

Take the walk
to the open door,
this is where you
find out more
about the stars,
oceans, quakes,
dragons, cars,
cheetahs, snakes,
unicorns, and
jumping beans,
horses, bugs,
and time machines.
From killer whales,
and free-tailed bats,
to hammer heads
and kitty cats,
the library has got a book.
Come on in,
take a look.
Learn how to cook
or write a poem.
Read it here
or take it home.
What do you want to learn about?
It's free!
It's here!
Check it out!

RECESS
by **Avis Harley**

Some play soccer,
some run races.
Others read
in quiet places.

Some find leaves
or draw with chalk.
Some play tag,
while others talk.

A few play chess.
Lots play ball.
And some just like
to watch it all.

Take 5!

1. **Read this poem aloud while pantomiming some of the motions** suggested in the poem (like kicking, running, reading, drawing, talking).

2. Read the poem aloud again, and this time **invite students to chime in on the repeated word** *some*. Create a simple cue card with the word *some* on it to alert students to say it out loud each time it occurs (five times!).

3. For discussion: *What is your favorite thing to do at recess?*

4. Repetition is a key ingredient in creating poems. Sometimes a poet uses repetition not just to enhance the sound of the poem, but to emphasize meaning. **Lead the students in discussing how the poet repeats the word *some* in this poem to show the many choices for recess activities.**

5. Compare this poem with another poem entitled **"Recess" by Michele Krueger** (3rd Grade, Week 2, page 148). Do the poets highlight any of the same activities?

Take 5!

1. **This is a poem that lends itself perfectly to full-body involvement** while reading it aloud. Try doing some of the actions described in the poem (swinging a baseball bat, running, huffing and puffing, aching feet).

2. **In sharing the poem aloud again, students can say the column of words** (*I / can't / even / catch / my / breath*), breathing deeply between each word to suggest breathless running, while you read the rest of the poem aloud.

3. For discussion: ***What are some of your favorite things to do AFTER school?***

4. Discuss with students how many poems rhyme, but not all. This poem is an example of *free verse*. It doesn't rhyme, but **guide students in seeing how the poet arranges the lines** to highlight the column of single words right in the middle.

5. Follow up with an acrostic poem about playing baseball, **"Last Try" by Avis Harley** (1st Grade, Week 31, page 97).

THE WINNER
by **Georgia Heard**

Evenings,
we play ball
next to the creek
in our neighbor's field.

We run so fast

I
can't
even
catch
my
breath.

When blue dusk turns to black,
cold grass aches our feet,
trees creep close—
game's over.
Night wins!

MY PET
by **David L. Harrison**

See those bats?
In the maple tree?
The one on the left
Belongs to me.

Haven't told him yet
He's my pet.

He hangs all day
Napping with friends,
Then at dusk
When day ends

He spends the dark night
In silent flight,

A hungry shadow
Sweeping the skies
Wolfing down
Mosquitoes and flies.

Haven't told him yet
I love my pet.

Take 5!

1. To set the stage before reading this poem aloud, make an origami bat. A simple model is available here at nickrobinson.info/ origami/ diagrams/bat.htm. **After reading the poem aloud, hang the bat upside down.**

2. Read the poem again, and this time **invite students to chime in on the second and final stanzas in whisper voices** while you read the rest aloud.

3. For discussion: *If you could have any pet that's not usually a pet, what would it be?*

4. **Guide students in identifying the rhyming words** in this poem (*tree/me; yet/pet; friends/ends; night/flight; skies/flies*). Read the poem out loud again, and display the poem so students can join in on the rhyming words.

5. Compare this with another poem, **"Bat" by X. J. Kennedy** (1st Grade, Week 8, page 74), or a selection from *A Fuzzy-Fast Blur: Poems about Pets* by Laura Purdie Salas.

Take 5!

1. If possible, **bring a ball of yarn as a poetry prop** to show before reading this poem aloud in a quiet whisper voice. Add actions suggested by the poem's words (like sneaking on tiptoe, jumping, pouncing, leaping, hiding, sleeping).

2. Read the poem aloud again, **inviting students to mimic you in the same motions and actions** that correspond with the poem.

3. For discussion: *Where is the quietest place you like to go?*

4. Alternating lines end with rhyming words in this poem. **Pause before the final rhyming word in each pair** (*house/mouse; leaping/ sleeping*) and invite students to complete the rhyme. Use motions and gestures to guide their guesses. Guide them in talking about how the poem creates a picture of the kitty's activities, particularly with the words *leaping* and *sleeping*.

5. Look for **"What's the Opposite..."** **by Ann Whitford Paul** (5th Grade, Week 4, page 230), or selections from *A Curious Collection of Cats* by Betsy Franco.

ALL WORN OUT
by **Kristy Dempsey**

Tippy-toe, Kitty Cat
is sneaking through the house,
pushing on a puff of yarn,
wishing for a mouse.
Kitty loves to play all day,
jumping, pouncing, leaping.
Where is kitty hiding now?
Shh! Kitty's sleeping.

THE WOODLAND VOLE
by **Ken Slesarik**

The Woodland Vole
prefers to stroll,
walking leisurely.

A tiny soul,
the Woodland Vole,
don't chase it, let it be.

The Woodland Vole
just doesn't know,
when fleeing fast and free,

how very slow,
the Woodland Vole
can seem to you and me.

Take 5!

1. To prepare for reading the poem aloud, **display an image of a woodland vole and talk about this unique, mouse-sized animal** that lives in the woods and loves apples. Search Flickr.com or other sources for quick images to share.

2. **The title, "The Woodland Vole," is repeated in each stanza of the poem—the ideal opportunity for students to chime in** on that line as you read the rest of the poem aloud again.

3. For discussion: *What does it feel like to be small?*

4. The repeated use of the title, "The Woodland Vole," is a key building block in this poem. Each stanza in this poem includes an end-rhyme with the word *vole*—even a "slant" rhyme or "almost" rhyme in *vole* and *know* and *vole* and *slow*. **Challenge the kids to identify each rhyming pair (*vole/stroll; soul/vole; vole/know; slow/vole*) and then share the whole poem aloud again.**

5. Pair this poem with another about a small, slow creature, **"The World's Most Ancient Ant" by Jack Prelutsky** (Kindergarten, Week 6, page 32).

THE STAR-NOSED MOLE
by **Leslie Bulion**

Take 5!

1. **Show images of the star-nosed mole**, a hamster-sized mammal with 22 pink tentacles around its mouth. Search AnimalSpot.net or other sources for helpful images. You may also need to introduce a few key words (*peculiar, morsel, marshy, re-inhales, scents, larval, prey*).

2. Read the poem aloud again and incorporate actions (like **using your hands as waving tentacles** around your mouth, snorting, inhaling, snapping), and invite students to mimic your movements.

3. Sometimes poets weave facts into their poems. Guide students in talking about **the star-nosed mole in the water and on land.**

4. Sometimes poets like to use several words that start with the same sound (*alliteration*) to add to the sound of the poem. **Challenge students to identify repeated sounds** (*f, m, s, t*) and then list or highlight the words that begin with this sound (for example, *fleshy fingers; Mole's marshy meal; scents of snails; tweezer teeth*). Read the poem aloud together, emphasizing these words in particular.

5. For contrast, share **"Humpback Whale" by Jane Yolen** (4th Grade, Week 7, page 193).

The star-nosed mole's
Peculiar snout
(Pink, fleshy fingers
Fanning out)
Is full of nerves,
To find by feel,
Each morsel for
Mole's marshy meal.

But first, mole snorts,
Then re-inhales,
Air bubbles, bringing
Scents of snails,
And crayfish,
Tadpoles,
Minnows,
Bugs,
Earthworms,
Larval insects,
Slugs.

That nose-star hides
Mole's mouth beneath,
Which sports a set of
Tweezer teeth,
To snap up prey
At lightning speeds,
A skill each hungry
Star-nose
Needs.

Note: The star-nosed mole spends much of its marshy life underground, but loves to swim and hunt in the water.

HOW BIG IS THE ATLAS MOTH?
by **Deborah Ruddell**

If she settles in the middle
of the pillow on your bed,
you'll barely have a corner left
to rest your tired head.

Of *course*, you'll be uncomfortable,
but still—for what it's worth—
you'll get to share your pillow with
THE BIGGEST MOTH ON EARTH!

Take 5!

1. A bit of **background information will help students understand and enjoy this poem** even more. For example, the Atlas moth has a wingspan of 10-12 inches! If possible, show images of the Atlas moth found on KidsButterfly.org, or bring a pillowcase (or draw the outline of one, 21" x 32") to demonstrate the scale of the moth against the pillowcase.

2. While reading the poem aloud, use hand motions (fanning palms, stretching fingers, touching thumbs) to suggest the flying of the moth. Invite students to join in on the big finale line at the end, *THE BIGGEST MOTH ON EARTH!*, while bringing your fanning hands to rest near your head.

3. For discussion: *What is the biggest creature you have ever seen?*

4. Rhythm is a key element in this poem. Like a composer with the notes of a song, poets give their poems a beat, too. **Invite students to tap the rhythm of the poem** as you share it out loud again.

5. Share another rhythmic poem about an animal in the house, **"My Kitchen Was Invaded" by Jack Prelutsky** (3rd Grade, Week 12, page 158), or selections from *The Monarch's Progress: Poems with Wings* by Avis Harley.

Take 5!

1. **Alert students to the use of questions** and question marks in this poem, beginning with the title itself. Read the poem aloud slowly and with a questioning voice.

2. Read the poem aloud again, and **invite students to say the word** *weather* each time it occurs in the poem.

3. For discussion: ***What other weather questions do you wonder about?***

4. This poem uses several words that begin with the letters *w* and *r*. See if students can identify each of those *w* and *r* words (*wondered, why, weather, what, ways, watch, whether; rainbows, race, rays, raindrops, rose*). **Point out that poets use this technique of** *alliteration* to add to the sound qualities of the poem. Read the poem aloud again, emphasizing these words.

5. Follow up with another weather poem full of questions, **"Wondering" by Cynthia Cotten** (3rd Grade, Week 9, page 155), or a selection from *Sharing the Seasons*, edited by Lee Bennett Hopkins.

WHY DOES WEATHER?
by **Mary Quattlebaum**

Have you ever wondered why
Weather always comes from sky?
Why can't weather come from ground
And snow go up instead of down?

What if weather changed its ways?
We'd hurdle rainbows, race on rays,
And skip the clouds that lined the street
As raindrops rose beneath our feet.

Watch that weather! It just might
Twist and turn and wrongside right.
I wonder whether, if it could,
Weather ever, ever would.

CRUNCH
by **Debbie Levy**

Chatty Charlene enjoys food that crunches,
carrots and croutons and nuts were her lunches,
breadsticks and celery and radishes at night,
granola with apples and toast at first light.

But one day Charlene said, "This is too much!
"The carrots and croutons and apples and such—
"The noise of the chewing,
the *CRACK, CRANK,* and *CREAK,*
"is so loud in my head I can't hear myself speak!"

And that's why Charlene changed the food that she eats
to soft stuff like puddings and well-boiled meats.
It's sad, since Charlene is a mushy-food-hater.
Too bad no one told her:
Chew first and chat later.

Take 5!

1. **Munch with a flourish on something crunchy** before reading this poem aloud.

2. **Invite students to say the words in capital letters** in the poem (*CRACK, CRANK, and CREAK*) while you read the rest aloud.

3. For discussion: *What is your favorite crunchy food?*

4. Sometimes poets use words that mimic sounds (*onomatopoeia*). **Challenge the students to recognize the sound words** in this poem (such as *CRACK, CRANK, CREAK*), then read the poem aloud again.

5. Connect with **"Snack Rules" by Robyn Hood Black** (1st Grade, Week 10, page 76).

Take 5!

1. **Build a paper taco from construction paper** while you read the poem aloud. It's fine if some pieces fall out while you read!

2. Next, **invite students to echo read the poem, repeating each line after you read it aloud.**

3. For discussion: *What are your favorite kinds of tacos and taco ingredients?*

4. **Show how rhyming words help turn this list of ingredients into a poem.** Ask students: What are the words that rhyme (*corn/torn; row/below; slivers/river; bit/it*). Point out how sometimes the rhyme depends on the final syllable (*row/below*).

5. Follow up with the poem **"Avocado" by Constance Levy** (4th Grade, Week 11, page 197).

A TASTE OF TACO
by **Rebecca Kai Dotlich**

We feast on crackly
shells of corn;
tomatoes diced,
lettuce torn,
and onions in
a snow-white row
    crumble
to the plate below.

Spicy meat,
cheesy slivers,
fiery red sauce
spills
a river;
a dribble of a taco bit—
before we spoon
the rest of it.

BACKYARD SWING
by **X.J. Kennedy**

No matter how hard I pump my swing,
I don't fly over anything.
All I can see when I go high
Is buildings blotting out the sky.

But the knotholes in our old board fence—
I swing up close, they look immense.

Take 5!

1. Before sharing this poem, **introduce any unfamiliar words** such as *blotting*, *knotholes*, or *immense*. Read the poem aloud, pausing dramatically before the final stanza.

2. **Involve the students in a choral reading** by having them raise their hands and say *I* each time that word occurs in the poem (five times). Cue them by pointing to your eye.

3. **Discuss student swing preferences**: hard swing, soft swing, tire swing, other.

4. Every two lines in this poem end in rhyming words. **Lead students in identifying those rhyming words** (*swing/ anything; high/sky; fence/ immense*) and talk about how they may vary in syllable length (*swing/anything*) and in spelling the sounds (*high/sky; fence/immense*). Read the poem aloud together again, emphasizing these words in particular.

5. Share another poem about being outdoors, **"My Tree House" by Charles Ghigna** (1st Grade, Week 12, page 78).

Take 5!

1. **Talk briefly about your own family**—number of parents, sisters, brothers, pets—and ask students to think about their own family situations. Then read this poem aloud with zest, pausing briefly between each stanza.

2. To double the audible fun of this poem, **invite students to echo read the two middle stanzas** of this poem, repeating each line after you say it out loud. Read it slowly first, then try it again fast, just for fun.

3. For discussion: *What chores do you do around your house?*

4. **The repeated number words (*two, double*) are the key components** that make this poem interesting. Talk with the students about how repeating these words adds emphasis to both the sounds and the meaning of the words. Read the poem aloud together again—twice!

5. Follow up with **Michael Salinger's "My Noisy Family"** (3rd Grade, Week 17, page 163), or with other family poems from *A Suitcase of Seaweed* by Janet Wong.

DOUBLE THE TROUBLE
by **Janet Wong**

My family
is made up of

two mothers,
two fathers,
two sisters,
two brothers,
two dogs,
and two cats
in two
different houses

with double
the shopping
and double
the laundry
and double
the trouble
and double
the noise—

and twice as much
love for us
girls and us boys.

FIRE STATION
by **Sara Holbrook**

This is the place
firefighters
polish and sweep.
Roll hoses,
sit, sleep.
Store coats,
boots, supplies,
where they munch down
snacks
and exercise,
until
Briiiinnnng!
the call.
Sirens wail.
Grabbing gear
from the wall.
Jump on board.
Horns blast.
Doors come up.
Take off fast.
It's never at a time
they choose.
Just.
Hurry. Quick.
No time to lose.
Ladders, axes,
masks and tanks.
They answer the call,
and we say,
THANKS!

Take 5!

1. **Challenge students to listen for the sound word in the poem** (*Briiiinnnng!*). Read the poem slowly and deliberately until the word *Briiiinnnng!,* and the rest quickly until you pause for the final line, *THANKS!*

2. **Students can say the sound word** (*Briiiinnnng!*) and the final word (*THANKS!*) dramatically while you read the rest of the poem.

3. **Talk about the proper use of the 911 emergency phone line** and fire safety procedures at school and at home.

4. Poets love to play with words and how they are arranged on the page. Here the poem is almost like a list with key words used to paint a picture in your mind. Guide the students in identifying the rhyming words (*sweep/sleep; supplies/ exercise, etc.*) and "almost" or "slant" rhymes (*wail/wall*) in the poem. **Talk about those vivid words that help you imagine a fire station** (such as *sirens, horns, ladders, axes*).

5. Connect this poem with **"Fire!" by Laura Purdie Salas** (1st Grade, Week 14, page 80).

BUBBLE GUM
by **Greg Pincus**

Bubble gum is very yummy
In your mouth
But not your tummy

Take 5!

1. Before sharing this poem, mimic chewing a piece of gum with gusto and then read the poem aloud. **Point to your mouth and nod for the second line, and then pat your stomach and shake your head for the third line.**

2. Next, **divide the students into two groups—one to read the second line and one to read the third line. You begin by reading the first line aloud.** Read the poem aloud with everyone using the same gestures (pointing to mouth and nodding, patting stomach and shaking head).

3. **Survey the students about their favorite sugary and sugar-free treat preferences.**

4. **This simple poem relies on one rhyme (*yummy/tummy*) and a simple contrast (good/bad) for** its impact. Talk about this with the students, and end with reading or saying the poem aloud in unison.

5. Look for another short poem by **Greg Pincus, "First"** (1st Grade, Week 28, page 94).

CHRISTMAS IS
by **George Ella Lyon**

Mamaw, Papaw
Aunt Pepperlou

Cousin Susan
and Uncle Froggie, too

Neighbor David
from across the street

Mama lighting candles
Daddy carving meat

Best china
shining on the cloth

Dinner slower
than a three-toed sloth!

Take 5!

1. Add a bit of fun to sharing this poem with poetry props. Bring a simple placemat or tablecloth, a few dishes, silverware, a napkin, and a cup or glass, and dramatize setting the table before you read this poem aloud. Afterward, **talk about the family names in the poem and what a** *three-toed sloth* **might be.**

2. Next, **invite students to echo read** the poem, repeating each line after you read it aloud.

3. For discussion: *What are some of your family's favorite holiday traditions?*

4. Help students find the rhyming pairs of words that sound alike (*Pepperlou/too; street/meat; cloth/sloth*). Display the poem and then read it aloud again, and **point to the rhyming word as students chime in to complete each rhyme.**

5. Connect this poem with another one about food, family, and neighbors, **"Mrs. Betty" by Rebecca Kai Dotlich** (Kindergarten, Week 14, page 40).

AFTER SLEDDING
by **Betsy Franco**

The kettle sings—
wheee, heee!
A cocoa treat
fills all our cups.

Shivery cold,
we grab a quilt
and huddle close,
all bundled up.

Whooo, whooo—
the wind builds up.
The winter whistle
of a storm.

Crackle, spit—
the fire glows.
We sip and giggle,
cozy warm.

Take 5!

1. As you read this poem, hold a mug and pretend to sip as if the beverage were very hot. **Add shivering and huddling motions while reading the poem aloud.**

2. Next, read the poem aloud again, and **invite students to say the sound words in the poem (*Wheee, heee; Whooo, whooo; crackle, spit*)** while you read the rest aloud. Cue students by holding up your mug when it's their turn.

3. For discussion: ***What are some of your favorite things to do on a cold day?***

4. Challenge the students to **see if they recognize the sound words in this poem (*Wheee, heee; Whooo, whooo; crackle, spit*)** and talk about what other words the poet might have chosen. Then read the poem aloud again, with students chiming in to highlight the sound words.

5. Share another poem about waiting out a storm, **"Stormy Day" by Rebecca Kai Dotlich** (Kindergarten, Week 17, page 43) or selections from *Winter Trees* by Carole Gerber.

MOMMA'S TRYING
by **Janet Wong**

Momma's trying
to lose weight
even though
we've told her
she looks great.

She says
it's not just looks
that matter.
She wouldn't care
if she were fatter

but she wants
to be healthy,
she wants
to be strong,
so she can live

a long, long,
long, long,
long, long time
(and visit me
when she's 99)!

Take 5!

1. **Read this poem aloud with exercising motions** like stretching, reaching, and bending.

2. **Ask for six volunteers to help read the poem aloud**, one volunteer for each time the word *long* appears in the final stanza. Display the words of the poem, or simply point to each student in turn to say the word as you read the rest of the poem aloud.

3. For discussion: *What are your favorite choices for healthy snacks?*

4. Sometimes a poet uses repetition for emphasis and added meaning. **Guide the students in talking about how the poet repeats the word *long* in this poem** to underline the mother's desire to be healthy for her child.

5. Match this poem with **"Sack Lunch" by Charles Waters** (Kindergarten, Week 11, page 37), or selections from *The Rainbow Hand: Poems about Mothers and Children* by Janet Wong.

Take 5!

1. Kick off the oral reading of this poem by asking students: *Do you dream at night? Do you remember your dreams in the morning?* This poet wonders about dreams, too. Read the poem aloud, pausing a bit between stanzas.

2. The key word *dream* appears in each stanza. **Invite the students to chime in** on that word only as you read the rest of the poem aloud.

3. For discussion: *If you could plan your dream at night, what would you like to dream about?*

4. Lead the students in discussing how the poet repeats the word *dream* and the **use of questions to create a feeling of wonder.**

5. Combine this poem with **"They Call It 'Science'" by Stephanie Calmenson** (Kindergarten, Week 24, page 50).

DREAMLAND
by **Carole Boston Weatherford**

Do dreams lurk in corners like a top-secret spy
or under a stairway that kisses the sky?

Do dreams pop in windows or wait in the hall
to pounce on the bed and bounce off the wall?

Why are some dreams in color, some, black-and-white,
some about falling, and some about flight?

And why do dreams fade in the blink of an eye
till you can't remember, hard as you try?

LIZARD AND CHAMELEON
by J. Patrick Lewis

Sitting still, taking in the sun
for fun
are a *Lizard* and a *Chameleon.*
The *Lizard* sits and sits and sits,
staring
at a *Chameleon* in different suits,
wearing
different colors to confuse
his foes.
Poor *Lizard* wishes he could change
his clothes.

Take 5!

1. Introduce the word *chameleon* and describe this animal. You'll find information at TheReptileReport.com. Then **read the poem aloud, using a low-pitched voice for the lizard** (lines 5, 6, 11, 12), **a high-pitched voice for the chameleon** (lines 7-10), and a normal voice for the rest (lines 1-4).

2. **Invite students to say the words *lizard* and *chameleon*** when they occur in the poem as you read the rest aloud.

3. **Discuss the concept of camouflage** and how the chameleon can change to *different colors to confuse his foes.*

4. **This poem uses rhyme in an unusual way, breaking up lines and rhyming parts of words,** rather than the usual rhyming of ends of lines. Guide students in finding the rhymes (*fun/-eon; staring/wearing; foes/clothes*) and rereading the lines.

5. Connect this poem with other poems by **J. Patrick Lewis** that compare two creatures, **"Frog and Toad"** (Kindergarten, Week 21, page 47) and **"Gnat and Flea"** (1st Grade, Week 27, page 93).

WEEK 21: LOVE & FRIENDSHIP

Take 5!

1. **Pretend you are a dog as you read this poem from a dog's point of view. Use a gravelly voice** and give extra effort to the first and last lines!

2. **Read the poem aloud again, inviting students to join you in making the dog noises** in the first two lines and wagging their "tails" in the last line.

3. For discussion: *What kind of Valentine might a cat send?*

4. We sometimes use one word to describe making a sound (such as *bark*) and another word to describe the sound itself (*woof*). **Challenge the students to find the sound words that capture dog noises in this poem (*woof, bark, arff, growl, grrr, ruff*).** Then read the poem aloud again to see and hear how sounds can become words.

5. Match this with another Valentine poem, **"Ingredients for a Valentine" by Bobbi Katz** (1st Grade, Week 21, page 87), or with more dog holiday poems from *Every Day's a Dog's Day: A Year in Poems* by Marilyn Singer.

MY DOG JACK THINKS UP HIS VALENTINE
by Patricia Hubbell

I could woof it, bark it, arff it . . .
I could growl it, grrr it, ruff it . . .

I could bring her balls, or bones, or rocks,
Fetch her paper, slippers, socks.
I could send my paw-print through the mail . . .

(But I think that I'll just
Wag my tail!)

FORGIVE AND FORGET
by Janet Wong

Forgive: OK.
It's a brand new day.

Forget?
Not yet.

Still upset?
You bet!

Take 5!

1. **Read this poem aloud slowly, with exaggerated facial expressions and simple gestures that match the lines of the poem** (for example, shrug, nod, shrug, shake your head, raise your shoulders, and nod).

2. Read the poem aloud again, **inviting students to chime in with the answers to each question (OK in line 1; Not yet in line 4; You bet! in line 6)** while you read the rest.

3. For discussion: **Which is harder, asking forgiveness or forgiving someone?**

4. Help students find the rhyming words that occur at the end of each pair of lines (OK/ day; forget/yet; upset/bet). **Talk about how the word pairs do not have the same number of syllables, and how the two-syllable words depend on the final syllable for their rhyme.**

5. Follow up with another poem about friendship by **Janet Wong, "The Do Kind"** (3rd Grade, Week 21, page 167).

Take 5!

1. **Locate Africa on a world map** and talk briefly about the variety of countries and cultures on that continent.

2. **Read the poem aloud again and pause before the last word** in each two-line stanza. Invite students to supply the rhyming word to end each stanza.

3. **Discuss some of the different backgrounds represented in your school** and community.

4. Help students find rhyming pairs of words that sound alike at the end of each two-line stanza (*place/face; Nile/child; trees/breeze; white/night; land/hand; vines/mines; drum/from; away/stay*). Talk about how the pattern of description in each stanza (beginning with *it's*) paints a picture in your mind. **Challenge students to notice examples of picture words** (*pyramid, coconuts, zebra striped black and white*, etc.).

5. Connect this poem with **"Cold War" by Margarita Engle** (5th Grade, Week 23, page 249) or *Roots and Blues: A Celebration* by Arnold Adoff.

AFRICA'S CHILD
by **Carole Boston Weatherford**

Africa's not just some far-off place.
It's the beat of your heart and the sun in your face.

It's grand, old pyramids near the river Nile
and elders naming a newborn child.

It's coconuts dangling from tops of trees
and grasses dancing in the breeze.

It's herds of zebra striped black and white,
and mighty lions that stalk at night.

It's the elephant, giant of the land.
It's cloth and baskets made by hand.

It's chimpanzees on jungle vines,
and riches deep in the darkest mines.

It's the *thump, thump, thump* of a talking drum.
It's where man's march first started from.

No, Africa's not so far away
for it is inside us to stay.

APPY BIRTHDAY
by **April Halprin Wayland**

Here's a cake for you with candles,
you can even blow them out!
There's no sticky frosting mess here,
there's no fancy birthday wrap.
It's a cake I made for you, dear,
with the Birthday Cake Bake app.

Take 5!

1. Before reading this poem aloud, **show a picture of a birthday cake from an e-card, app, or other electronic image** on your computer, cell phone, iPad, or other device.

2. Now **try reading the poem aloud in a monotone robot voice**, just for fun. Invite students to echo you on the final line for added emphasis.

3. For discussion: *What is your favorite app (application) or electronic (video) game?*

4. **Invite students to tap the rhythm of the poem as you share it again.** Like a composer with the notes of a song, poets give their poems a beat, too. In fact, this poem has a rhythm that fits the beat of "Twinkle, Twinkle, Little Star." Display the words of the poem and try singing it together to that tune.

5. Pair this with another poem about technology and friendship, **"Vacation Communication" by Carol-Ann Hoyte** (3rd Grade, Week 24, page 170), which can also be sung to the tune of "Twinkle, Twinkle, Little Star."

Take 5!

1. **The perfect poetry prop for this poem is a simple musical triangle.** See if you can locate one and "ping" it rhythmically while reading this poem aloud.

2. **Invite students to say the sound words** in the poem (*Ting! Ting!; Ring-a-ling!*) while you read the rest aloud. Cue students by tapping the triangle when it's their turn.

3. For discussion: *What other musical instruments make a ringing sound?*

4. Sometimes poets use each letter of a key word to begin the line of the poem, which is called *acrostic poetry*. Highlight the first words of each line in this poem to **show how the letters of TRIANGLE were used to shape the poem.** Challenge students to identify the rhyming pairs in this poem (*ting/Ring-a-ling!; Noise/enjoys*).

Look for more acrostic poems such as **"Crayons" by Ann Whitford Paul** (Kindergarten, Week 31, page 57), **"Last Try" by Avis Harley** (1st Grade, Week 31, page 97), or selections from *African Acrostics* by Avis Harley.

MUSIC LESSON
by **Laura Purdie Salas**

Ting! Ting!
Ring-a-ling!
I
Am silver
Noise.
Gently,
Lightly, make me chime for songs the
Ear enjoys!

HALF-PAST NEVER
by Lesléa Newman

When elephants wear dungarees
And snakes and monkeys grow on trees,
When hippos slide downhill on skis
And sleighs are pulled by bumblebees,
When sharks crawl on their hands and knees
And bats say "Bless you" when they sneeze,
When ostriches sing melodies
Composed by tiny circus fleas,
When cats and dogs speak Japanese
And swim across the seven seas,
When dinosaurs say "Pretty please,"
That's when I will eat my peas.

Take 5!

1. Take a moment to **encourage students to close their eyes and imagine this crazy collection of animals**: elephants in blue jeans, hippos on skis, and singing ostriches. Then continue by reading this poem aloud. You may need to explain what *dungarees* are.

2. Read the poem aloud again and **invite students to say the last line out loud together**.

3. For discussion: *What is your least favorite food?*

4. In this nonsensical, humorous poem, every single line rhymes with the same ending sound (*eez*). **Talk with students about each rhyming word and all the different ways those ending sounds are spelled** (*dungarees, trees, skis, bumblebees, knees, sneeze, melodies, fleas, Japanese, seas, please, peas*).

5. Share another silly poem with a surprise ending, **"Eight-year-old Uncle" by X. J. Kennedy** (3rd Grade, Week 26, page 172).

SPANISH EARS
by Carmen T. Bernier-Grand

How come the spellchecker
does not catch my mistakes?
I know you *fill* out a form
not *feel* it out.
I know you mow the *lawn*
not the *loan*.
When my Spanish ears learn
to hear those sounds
I will design a spellchecker
for you and me.

Take 5!

1. **Before sharing this poem, admit a mistake you have made in mispronouncing or misunderstanding a word.** Then read the poem aloud, emphasizing the words *fill, feel, lawn,* and *loan,* in particular. You might need to explain what a *spellchecker* is.

2. **Read the poem aloud again and invite students to say the words *fill, feel, lawn,* and *loan* in the poem. Cue students by pointing to your ear.

3. For discussion: *How do you feel when you make a mistake?*

4. Discuss with students that many poems rhyme, but not all. **This poem is an example of *free verse.* It doesn't rhyme, but guide students in seeing how the lines and line breaks build to create a poem.**

5. Follow up with another poem about words, **"Look It Up!" by Heidi Bee Roemer** (3rd Grade, Week 27, page 173).

I MIGHT GO TO MARS
by Juanita Havill

Me: "See you later, Mom.
I'm going to the moon."

Mom: "And I'm fixing lunch.
Be back by noon."

Me: "I might go to Mars."

Mom: "I don't think so."

Me: "You would if you knew
how fast I go."

Mom shrugs and frowns,
gives me that look.

So I tell her my secret:
I travel by book.

Take 5!

1. **Double-check that students know that Mars is in outer space**, a detail that makes a big difference in this poem. Then read the poem aloud, using a high-pitched, youthful voice for the lines for *Me,* a lower, authoritative voice for the lines for *Mom,* and your normal voice for the final stanza.

2. **Invite students to read the *Me* lines in unison.** If possible, display the words of the poem to assist students.

3. For discussion: *Where would you like to go if you could go absolutely anywhere?*

4. **This is a poem written for two voices or characters as if it were a conversation.** Consider how the ending rhymes (*moon/noon; so/go; look/book*) help make what could be simply dialogue a rhyming poem.

5. For another poem for two voices, look for **"The Way You Sound" by John Grandits** (4th Grade, Week 13, page 199).

Take 5!

1. Read this poem aloud while pantomiming the actions suggested by the poem **(fill a pot, stir, weigh ingredients, add things to the pot, stir)**.

2. Read the poem again, and this time **invite students to say three key lines in the poem—Wait** (line 6), **Choose** (line 14), **and listen** (line 22)—while you read the rest of the poem aloud.

3. For discussion: **What do you like to help cook or bake?**

4. **Challenge students to identify words or phrases that help the reader or listener imagine this scene** (for example, *boil, simmer, a hammer, a kite, stretch like taffy*). Talk about those images and then share the poem aloud again.

5. For another cooking poem, look for **"Who Invented Cookies?" by Joan Bransfield Graham** (Kindergarten, Week 10, page 36).

RECIPE FOR A POEM
by **Kristy Dempsey**

Fill a pot
with red-hot thought.
Boil a bit,
Simmer.
Let sit.
Wait . . .
some more.
Open a drawer,
pick a spoon,
a hammer,
a kite,
anything might
be of use.
Choose.
Weigh the contents.
Stir the depths.
Season with truth and
a dash of laughter.
Stretch like taffy,
Slice into bites.
Throw to the wind
and listen.

ROUGH AND TUMBLE
by **Lesléa Newman**

See them leap into the air,
See them jump upon a chair.
See them run and see them leap,
See them land into a heap.
See them roll and see them vault,
See them do a somersault.
See them slide and see them slip,
See them do a triple flip.
See them as they start the chase,
See them dash from place to place.
See them romp and see them rumble,
Full of grace, they never stumble.
Are they athletes? Acrobats?
No, my dear, they're just our cats.

Take 5!

1. **Incorporate motions for some of the action words in this poem** (choose from *leap, jump, run, land, roll, somersault, slide, slip, flip, chase, dash, romp, rumble*).

2. The first 11 lines all begin with the words *See them*. **Invite students to say those words** while you repeat your pantomime performance and read the rest aloud.

3. For discussion: *If this poem describes cat behavior, how would you describe dog behavior?*

4. In this poem, **the poet also uses *alliteration*** to repeat the same sound in the beginning of several words for greater emphasis. Help students locate examples of alliteration (for example, *see, slide, slip; romp, rumble*).

5. Revisit a previous poem about cat antics, **"All Worn Out" by Kristy Dempsey** (2nd Grade, Week 5, page 111).

DOG WALKING TANKA
by **Margarita Engle**

sniff sniff
beyond the fence
my puppy
shows me how to enjoy
wildflowers

Take 5!

1. Add a bit of fun to sharing this poem with a bit of pantomiming as you read it aloud. **Move around the room while reading, sniffing the air, sniffing for flowers.**

2. If possible, display the words of the poem and **ask for five volunteers to help read the poem aloud**, one volunteer for each line of the poem with a brief pause between each line.

3. For discussion: *What else can we learn from pets?*

4. **This is an example of a poem form that usually does not rhyme —a tanka poem, similar to the haiku poem.** Originally a Japanese form of poetry, a tanka has five lines (generally 5 syllables, 7 syllables, 5 syllables, 7 syllables, 7 syllables). Note: Some poets prefer not to count syllables, but rather vary long and short lines to simply try to achieve "the feel" of a tanka. Guide students in understanding the tanka form with this example.

5. Connect this poem with a haiku poem, **"See-Saw" by Graham Denton** (1st Grade, Week 32, page 98).

OUTER SPACEMAN
by **Julie Larios**

He's as skinny as a toothpick
but as tall as a giraffe.
He laughs like a hyena—
if that's his laugh.
His eyes are like volcanoes,
he's as warty as a toad,
and he's standing right there
in the middle of the road.

Take 5!

1. Take a moment to encourage students to close their eyes and **imagine a creature from outer space**, someone super-skinny and tall, with big eyes and warty skin. You may need to explain key vocabulary like *hyena* and *warty*.

2. Read the poem aloud again and **pause dramatically before the last word in line 4 and line 8**. See if the students can guess the rhyming word to end line 4 (*laugh*) and line 8 (*road*).

3. For discussion: *What might an outer space*_kid_ *look like?*

4. Alternating lines end with rhyming words in this poem. Read the poem aloud, pausing before the final rhyming word in each pair (*giraffe/ laugh; toad/road*) and inviting students to complete the rhyme. Then lead a discussion of how **the poem creates a picture of this creature from outer space** comparing it to other things (*toothpick, giraffe, hyena, volcano,* and *toad*).

5. Revisit a previous space poem, **"I Might Go to Mars" by Juanita Havill** (2nd Grade, Week 28, page 134), or selections from *Imaginary Menagerie*, also by Julie Larios.

Take 5!

1. Feeling brave? **You can sing this poem to the tune of "On Top of Old Smoky."** Add facial expressions that correspond to the poem lines (*angry, sore, mad, laugh, sulk, fret, peeved, upset, grumble, glare, sullen, stare, confounded, confused*).

2. Sing it for the students first, then display the words and **invite them to join you, making the faces that go with the poem words.**

3. For discussion: ***What if vegetables had feelings?***

4. **Sometimes poets use their imaginations to guess what it might be like if something that is not alive had a real personality. This technique is called** *personification*. Guide the students in finding each word or line in this poem that suggests vegetables have human feelings. Also talk about the pun in the final line and the double meaning of the word *stew* (to be angry, or a thick soup).

5. Follow up with another food poem, **"Global Gorging" by Terry Webb Harshman** (4th Grade, Week 10, page 196), or selections from *Food Hates You, Too* by Robert Weinstock.

MY CARROTS ARE ANGRY
by **Jack Prelutsky**

My carrots are angry,
My scallions are sore.
My beans are so mad
They can't laugh anymore.
My radishes sulk,
And my artichokes fret.
My pumpkins are peeved,
And my peas are upset.

My cabbages grumble,
My broccoli glares.
My onions are sullen,
My celery stares.
Confounded, confused,
I don't know what to do
When all of my vegetables
Are in a stew.

PICK-UP TRUCK
by **Janet Wong**

We pile our stuff,
everything we own.

We pile it high
as it can go,

high as my uncle
can reach on tiptoes

standing in the back
of the truck.

Table, chairs, beds, and all—
Momma is praying it doesn't fall—

or we'll need to stop
and pick things up.

Is that why they call it
a pick-up truck?

Take 5!

1. **Read this poem aloud while pantomiming the packing and piling** suggested in the poem.

2. Next, **invite students to echo read the poem, repeating each line after you read it aloud.**

3. For discussion: *What are the best and worst parts about moving?*

4. Poets love to play with words. Sometimes they'll use a word just because they like the sound of it or the way it makes a picture in your mind. **Do the words (for example, *pile it high; high as my uncle / can reach on tiptoes*) make a picture in your mind?** Discuss those images.

5. Revisit a previous Momma poem by **Janet Wong**, **"Momma's Trying"** (2nd Grade, Week 18, page 124), and read selections from Wong's book *Behind the Wheel: Poems about Driving.*

Take 5!

1. This is a poem written for two voices. **Vary your tone of voice to reflect two points of view in reading the poem aloud.** Explain a few vocabulary words like *mites* and *sublime*.

2. **Invite students to join in by reading the left hand side of text while you read the right hand side. Everyone joins in on the final word *rain*.** Practice the turn-taking until it's smooth and easy.

3. For discussion: *Which do you like better, rainy days or sunny days?*

4. In this poem, the rhyming pairs of words crisscross from the part on the left to the part on the right and back again. **Challenge students to identify each rhyming pair** (*rot/hot; agree/me; sane/rain*) and even the "slant" or "almost" rhyme (*divine/sublime*).

5. Share another fun poem about weather, **"My Dog" by Charles Waters** (1st Grade, Week 9, page 75).

SUMMER SHOWERS
by **Carole Gerber**

I hate to get my feet wet.
Standing water makes me rot.

> And I *prefer* to stand in it—
> especially when I'm hot.

Well, I like showers better.

> They're refreshing, I agree.

Plus, they wash away the bugs
And mites that crawl all over me.

> I always turn my face up . . .

Me, too. It feels divine!

> It perks me up
> and greens my leaves.
> The moisture is sublime.

No matter how we get it,

> Any plant that's sane . . .

Welcomes Mother Nature's gift of . . .

> *Rain!*

THE SECRET SEED
by **Allan Wolf**

A seed holds tomorrow
inside her shell.
What will she be?
She will not tell.
To find out what,
you'll have to wait
and watch her grow
from grain to great.

Take 5!

1. **Heighten interest in this poem with a small poetry prop—a tiny seed of any kind or size.** Hold the seed in your hand and extend your hand open as you read the poem.

2. Next, **invite students to echo read the poem,** repeating each line after you read it aloud.

3. For discussion: *What kinds and sizes of seeds have you seen or planted?*

4. In this poem, alternating lines end with rhyming words. Guide students in identifying the rhyming pairs (*shell/tell; wait/great*). **Read the poem aloud again, pausing before the final rhyming word in each pair and inviting students to complete the rhyme.** Talk about what the words in the final line (*from grain to great*) suggest (growing from a tiny seed to something great).

5. Connect this poem with another poem about transformation, **"Tadpole Wishes" by Terry Webb Harshman** (Kindergarten, Week 7, page 33).

POEMS FOR THIRD GRADE

Common Core Standards
for Third Grade (RL.3.5)

In sharing poetry with third graders, we can support their growing vocabularies, promote their playful interaction with words and language, and develop their confidence in engaging with print.

First we focus on enjoyment and understanding, then we guide students in responding to poetry in various forms by exploring narrative poems that tell stories, lyrical poems that explore questions and emotions, and humorous poems that make us groan or laugh.

We can help students understand how poets use lines and stanzas to build poems in distinctive ways.

With this fun and participatory approach, we can celebrate poetry while gently introducing and reinforcing key skills.

THIRD GRADE

week 1	School	Funday, Imaginary 1st *by Heidi Mordhorst*
week 2	More School	Recess *by Michele Krueger*
week 3	Fun & Games	Fishing *by Janet Wong*
week 4	Pets	A Plague of Penguins *by Julie Larios*
week 5	More Pets	Spotty's Tongue *by Betsy Franco*
week 6	On the Ground	Flat Gray Rock *by Arnold Adoff*
week 7	In the Water	A Clam *by Jack Prelutsky*
week 8	In the Air	Bluebirds *by Jen Bryant*
week 9	Weather	Wondering *by Cynthia Cotten*
week 10	Food	Two Scoops *by Linda Sue Park*
week 11	More Food	Pumpkin *by Jane Yolen*
week 12	House & Home	My Kitchen Was Invaded *by Jack Prelutsky*
week 13	Families	The Breakfast Boss *by Janet Wong*
week 14	Community	Out My Window *by Amy Ludwig VanDerwater*
week 15	Stuff We Love	Lucky Penny *by Constance Levy*
week 16	Holidays	Little Village *by Terry Webb Harshman*
week 17	Time Together	My Noisy Family *by Michael Salinger*
week 18	Human Body	Catching a Yawn *by Avis Harley*
week 19	More Human Body	It's a Wrap *by Carol-Ann Hoyte*
week 20	Art & Colors	How the Birds Got Their Colors *by Joseph Bruchac*
week 21	Love & Friendship	The Do Kind *by Janet Wong*
week 22	A Kinder Place	Small Talk *by Ken Slesarik*
week 23	Exploring	Explorer *by Joan Bransfield Graham*
week 24	Science & Tech	Vacation Communication *by Carol-Ann Hoyte*
week 25	Song & Dance	Barnyard Ballet *by Jeannine Atkins*
week 26	Nonsense	Eight-year-old Uncle *by X.J. Kennedy*
week 27	World of Words	Look It Up! *by Heidi Bee Roemer*
week 28	Books	A Quiet Day *by Amy Ludwig VanDerwater*
week 29	Poetry Poems	Poem Like the Sea *by Patricia Hubbell*
week 30	RR&R	The Writer's Drill *by Esther Hershenhorn*
week 31	Different Forms	Catku *by Lee Wardlaw*
week 32	Metaphor & Simile	Honey *by J. Patrick Lewis*
week 33	Personification	Stapler *by Georgia Heard*
week 34	On the Move	Car Trip *by Juanita Havill*
week 35	Summer Vacation	My Best Friend Is Leaving *by Debbie Levy*
week 36	Looking Forward	Moon Buggy *by Juanita Havill*

"Between what I see and what I say,
Between what I say and what I keep silent,
Between what I keep silent and what I dream,
Between what I dream and what I forget,
Poetry."

⁕ Octavio Paz ⁕

Take 5!

1. Sit at a computer or with paper and pen and **pretend you're thinking about writing a letter.** Then read this poem aloud, pausing at the end of each letter component.

2. Read the poem aloud again and **invite students to read the heading** (*Funday, Imaginary 1st*), **greeting** (*Dear Daydream*), **closing** (*Sincerely*), **and signature** (*Me*) while you read the rest of the poem.

3. This is **a teachable moment for reviewing the parts of a friendly or personal letter.**

4. Point out that sometimes poets borrow patterns from other things, like letters, to create a poem. Here, the poet adds rhyme to turn a letter into a poem. **Guide students in identifying the rhyming pairs of words** (*friend/again; art/smart; me/P.E.*) and talk about how sometimes the rhyme depends on the final syllable (*friend/again; me/P.E.*), and how sometimes poets use an "almost" or "slant" rhyme (*friend/again*).

5. Follow up with another poem about school, **"Feeling Jumpy" by Patricia Hubbell** (4th Grade, Week 1, page 187).

FUNDAY, IMAGINARY 1ST
by **Heidi Mordhorst**

Funday, Imaginary 1st

Dear Daydream,

I'm glad you are my secret friend.
When will you tickle my brain again?
You're welcome in math, in science and art.
Your wondering wandering makes me smart.
Please come to visit and read with me.
Just don't interrupt when it's time for P.E.!

Sincerely,

Me

RECESS
by **Michele Krueger**

Climbing, sliding,
laughing, skipping,
cherry-flavored
fruit juice sipping

throwing, catching,
baseball smacking,
celery with peanut butter
crunchy snacking,

bouncing, giggling,
hopping, singing,
running, shouting,
up-high swinging,

walking, talking,
jump-rope turning,
'til it's time
to go back learning

Take 5!

1. **Try pantomiming some of the action words in the poem while you read it aloud** (*climbing, skipping, throwing, catching, bouncing, hopping, running, walking, jumping,* etc.).

2. Alert the students to all the action words in this poem (*climbing, sliding, throwing, catching,* etc.). **Display the words of the poem and invite students to choose their favorite action and chime in when that word appears.**

3. **Talk with students about their favorite recess and recreational activities.**

4. Show how rhyming words help turn this list of action words into a poem. Ask students to identify the words that rhyme (*skipping/sipping; smacking/snacking; singing/swinging; turning/learning*). **Read the poem aloud again. Pause before the final rhyming word in each pair and invite students to complete the rhyme.**

5. Pair this poem with another **"Recess"** poem **by Avis Harley** (2nd Grade, Week 2, page 108), or selections from Jack Prelutsky's *Good Sports*.

FISHING
by **Janet Wong**

Grandpa
is taking me fishing
tomorrow.
He's going to borrow
a boat.

How many catfish
can I catch?
Maybe a dozen
or a dozen
and a half.

Grandpa says
four fish
will be plenty.
But I want many,
many MORE!

Take 5!

1. Create a simple poetry prop to add a bit of fun. Attach a small magnet to the end of a piece of string or yarn about two feet long. Then tie the string to a ruler or short stick. Put a paper clip on the end of a cut-out paper fish, then go fishing. **Your fishing pole with magnet "hook" should pick up the paper clip fish** as you read the poem aloud.

2. Read the poem aloud again and **invite students to say the question line, *How many catfish / can I catch?*** while you read the rest.

3. For discussion: ***What are some things you especially enjoy doing with a grandparent*** (or with another family member)?

4. Poets give their poems shape in many ways. Read the poem aloud again and pause dramatically before each stanza. Talk with students about how **key words are used in each stanza to paint a picture in your mind** (*fishing, boat, catfish, four*).

5. Share another poem about spending time with grandparents also written by **Janet Wong, "Grandfather's Chopsticks"** (1st Grade, Week 11, page 77) or selections from John Frank's *How to Catch a Fish*.

A PLAGUE OF PENGUINS
by **Julie Larios**

Underpants with lots of penguins
p.j.'s packed with penguins, too—
I've got penguins on my hats
and coats
and shirts
and socks
and shoes.
Mom likes penguins everywhere—
my walls,
my lamp,
my sheets,
my pillow.
When I'm big I'll have one pet:
a perfectly nasty armadillo.

Take 5!

1. **As you read this poem aloud, point to various clothing items or objects mentioned in the poem** such as *coat, shirt, sock, shoe, wall,* or *lamp.*

2. For a fun choral reading, **coach the students to say the word** *penguin* **each time it pops up in the poem.** Display the words of the poem to guide student participation.

3. For discussion: ***What is your favorite animal?***

4. **Sometimes poets like to use many words that start the same (*alliteration*) to add to the sound of the poem.** Challenge students to identify a repeated sound in this poem (*p*) and then list and say the words that begin with this sound (*p.j.'s, packed, penguins*). Read this humorous poem aloud together again, emphasizing these words in particular.

5. Connect this poem with another about an armadillo and a pillow, **"Armadillo" by X. J. Kennedy** (1st Grade, Week 26, page 92).

Take 5!

1. **Encourage students to close their eyes and imagine a big, drooling dog** with his tongue hanging out, licking everyone and everything. Then read the poem aloud, pausing at the end of each stanza.

2. Read the poem aloud again, **inviting students to join in on the final line.**

3. For discussion: *What are the best and worst parts about having a pet?*

4. **This poem is a good example of humorous poetry.** Why is this funny? Ask the students! Responses will vary, but might include: the dog's name (*Spotty*), the dog's behavior (*kissing, drooling, tonguing the table, washing the baby, cleaning the floor*), the vivid words themselves (*drooling, tonguing, vacuum-like*), or the surprise ending.

5. Share another dog poem, **"Good Dog! Bad Dog!" by Jeannine Atkins** (5th Grade, Week 5, page 231).

SPOTTY'S TONGUE
by **Betsy Franco**

Spotty's been warned not to kiss any guest—
that drooling on visitors makes him a pest.

Spotty's been scolded for tonguing the table,
or washing the baby, although he's quite able.

But Spotty's encouraged to finish one chore:
his vacuum-like tongue cleans the dining room floor.

FLAT GRAY ROCK
by **Arnold Adoff**

Flat
Gray
Rock

At
Fence
Post
Corner   Of   The   Yard
Pull
Two   Hands   Hard   And
Lift
Flat
Rock

Roof
Of
Spider
House

Take 5!

1. If possible, **bring a large, flat rock as a prop** to set the stage. Read this poem aloud slowly and while making pulling and lifting motions.

2. Read the poem again and this time **invite students to say the words in lines 1 (*Flat*), 2 (*Gray*), and 3 (*Rock*), and then lines 10 (*Lift*), 11 (*Flat*), and 12 (*Rock*)**, with dramatic pauses after each line, while you read the rest of the poem aloud.

3. **Talk with students about their own discoveries under rocks or near fences.**

4. Sometimes poets use graphic components to add interest to their poems. Guide students in discussing how **here the poet uses capital letters, no punctuation, and distinctive spacing** to add to the impact of each stanza and to the poem overall.

5. Connect this poem with another poem about insects, **"Gnat and Flea" by J. Patrick Lewis** (1st Grade, Week 27, page 93), or selections from *Bug Off! Creepy Crawly Poems* by Jane Yolen.

A CLAM
by **Jack Prelutsky**

A clam is a creature
Of quiet aplomb.
In all situations
A clam remains calm.
A clam doesn't wander
Or move very much . . .
It's easy to think
That a clam's out of touch.

A clam doesn't care
To do dangerous deeds.
A quiet location
Is all a clam needs.
And so a clam rarely
Is subject to strife.
A clam simply **is**,
Which is not a bad life.

Take 5!

1. Feeling brave? **You can sing this poem** to the tune of "On Top of Old Smoky." Sing it for the students first, and then display the words and invite them to join you.

2. If you prefer to read the poem aloud, invite students to join in on the word *clam* each time it occurs in the poem. **They can clap their hands together each time they say *clam* to mimic the opening and shutting of the clamshell, too.**

3. Sometimes poets weave facts into their poems. **Guide students in noting what information we learn about clams** in this poem.

4. **This poem is an example of wordplay.** Guide students in seeing how the similarities between the words *clam* and *calm* inspired the poem.

5. Link this poem with **"Fish" by Joy Acey** (1st Grade, Week 4, page 70), or selections from *At the Sea Floor Café: Odd Ocean Critter Poems* by Leslie Bulion.

BLUEBIRDS
by **Jen Bryant**

I built a house
of sturdy wood;
I waited and waited
as long as I could.

Then one sunny day
in the first week of May,
two bluebirds flew in
and decided to stay.

So I waited and waited
and waited some more,
now instead of just two
those bluebirds are FOUR!

Take 5!

1. Read this poem aloud, but **pause before the final word in each stanza and challenge students to guess the missing word**.

2. Read the poem aloud again and display the words of the poem, if possible. This time **invite students to chime in when the word *waited* pops up** in the poem (five times!).

3. Talk with students about **bird-watching experiences** they may have had.

4. Poets use line breaks and stanzas to give their poems structure. **Read each stanza in this poem as if it were a separate poem.** Talk with students about each stanza and what it adds to the poem—facts, suspense, and surprise.

5. Match this poem with another bird poem, **"Bluejay Sings Two Different Songs" by Mary Lee Hahn** (Kindergarten, Week 8, page 34), or selections from *The Cuckoo's Haiku and Other Birding Poems* by Michael J. Rosen.

WONDERING
by **Cynthia Cotten**

How do birds know
it's going to snow?

When crowding to feed
on suet and seed,
are they merely responding
to air pressure dropping?

Or
is it more?

Do they hear a faint whisper,
a warning,
a call
that flakes will soon fall?

Is that how they know
it will snow?

Take 5!

1. **Read the poem aloud using a whisper voice for the fourth stanza.** You may need to explain the word *suet.*

2. Next, display the text of the poem, **inviting students to lead with the first stanza and close with the final stanza** while you read the rest aloud.

3. For discussion: *What signs of winter do we watch for?*

4. In this poem, the poet repeats the use of questions to build the poem. **Guide students in exploring how each stanza is a question** and how short and long questions are alternated to provide a structure for the poem.

5. Follow up with another weather poem that poses questions, **"Why Does Weather?" by Mary Quattlebaum** (2nd Grade, Week 9, page 115).

TWO SCOOPS
by **Linda Sue Park**

An ice-cream cone may seem at first
the best of things to eat.
Beware, beware! For danger lurks
within this icy treat.

The drips at first are innocent.
You catch them with your tongue.
Beware the menace in disguise!
They've only just begun.

From cone to hand, from hand to wrist,
the drips slip fast, then faster.
Beware, beware the peril of
an elbow-deep disaster:

A grownup will attack you!
With a napkin—oh, beware!
The napkin only smears the drips,
so now they're everywhere!

Survive the sticky meltdown of
that chocolate-chocolate chip.
Beware the challenge that awaits:
The dreaded TRIPLE dip!

Take 5!

1. **Add a bit of fun to sharing this poem with a poetry prop** —a paper ice cream cone with three round scoops.

2. In sharing the poem aloud again, **students can say the word *beware* with great drama each time it occurs.** Cue students by raising your fake ice cream cone!

3. **Survey students about their favorite ice cream flavors.**

4. This poem is another good example of humorous poetry. **Talk with students about how the poet creates humor in this poem by describing a funny experience with some exaggeration.** Pinpoint examples in the words and phrases the poet uses to create a scene in your mind.

5. Connect this poem with **"Who Invented Cookies?" by Joan Bransfield Graham** (Kindergarten, Week 10, page 36).

PUMPKIN
by Jane Yolen

Pumpkin begins all round
grown upon a dirty mound,
but when it's mashed up
into pies
it's still round.
Someone wise
needs to explain
that simple fact
that whether undone
or intact,
in a plate
or on the ground,
pumpkin
simply goes around.

Take 5!

1. After reading this poem aloud, **share this short video** about growing giant pumpkins: minnesota.publicradio.org/display/web/2011/10/18/pumpkin-video.

2. Read the poem aloud again and **invite students to chime in on line 5 (*it's still round*) and the final line (*simply goes around*).**

3. For discussion: *What are your favorite things about pumpkins?* (Their color or size, baking or eating pie, carving jack-o-lanterns, etc.)

4. Poets love to create images built from words and phrases. **Talk with students about how key words are used in this poem to paint a picture in your mind, particularly the words *round* and *around*.**

5. Challenge students with this poem about fall, **"Apprehended by Autumn" by Kristy Dempsey** (5th Grade, Week 9, page 235), or selections from *Pumpkin Butterfly: Poems from the Other Side of Nature* by Heidi Mordhorst.

MY KITCHEN WAS INVADED
by Jack Prelutsky

My kitchen was invaded
By a horde of nibbling mice.
They nibbled, nibbled, nibbled
On my peanuts, cheese, and rice.

I built a better mousetrap
To remove them from my house.
It didn't do a single thing—
They've made a better mouse.

Take 5!

1. Before reading this poem aloud, **introduce a few key words** essential to understanding the poem, such as *invaded* and *horde*.

2. In sharing the poem aloud again, **students can say line 3 (*They nibbled, nibbled, nibbled*) while you read the rest of the poem.**

3. **Invite students to share any plans they have made that backfired.**

4. **Help students find the rhyming pairs that occur at the end of the stanzas in this poem** (*mice/rice; house/mouse*). Display the poem, then read it aloud again and point to the rhyming word as students chime in to complete each rhyme.

5. Look for more poems by **Jack Prelutsky**, such as **"The World's Most Ancient Ant"** (Kindergarten, Week 6, page 32) or **"My Carrots Are Angry"** (2nd Grade, Week 33, page 139).

THE BREAKFAST BOSS
by **Janet Wong**

Mom wakes me up
when she leaves for work.
It's my job
to wake my brothers up
an hour later.
I gently say their names
once, twice, and a third time.
I could yank their blankets off
to get them up fast
but I let them sleep
until the doorbell rings.
It's our neighbor Cristina
who is two years older than me
but two inches shorter.
She is The Breakfast Boss of us:
she makes sure we eat our cereal
while she peels the boiled eggs
Mom left in the pot.
We gulp our juice,
grab our homework,
and race to school
like bullet trains full of fuel—
ready to zoom ahead!

Take 5!

1. Before reading this poem aloud, set the stage by **surveying students about who helped at home this morning** and in what ways.

2. This time, invite students to say line 3 together (*It's my job*), **with special emphasis on the word *my*,** as you read the rest aloud.

3. For discussion: ***What chores do you do at home?***

4. Discuss with students how many poems rhyme, but not all. **This poem is another example of free verse.** It doesn't rhyme, but guide students in seeing how the lines and line breaks build to create a poem. Talk about how each line contains another detail that helps you picture the morning routine.

5. Connect this poem with another about a helpful neighbor, **"Mrs. Betty" by Rebecca Kai Dotlich** (Kindergarten, Week 14, page 40).

OUT MY WINDOW
by Amy Ludwig VanDerwater

I look out my window.
I study my street
staring at faces
I may never meet.
I peer at the people
passing below.

I watch them.
I wonder—

Where will they go?
An old man is laughing.
A dog walks a girl.
Children in sneakers
chase after a squirrel.
Who is that lady?
Why does she cry?
Who is the little boy
waving goodbye?

I think about them.
Who they are.
What they love.

Do they think about me
looking down from above?

Take 5!

1. **Play a video or show a slide show of people walking or of people's faces** as you read this poem aloud. One possibility is at youtube.com/watch?v=ldnLxTablA8.

2. Now read the poem aloud again, but this time **incorporate nine volunteer readers, one for each italicized line.** You read all the rest of the lines slowly in a thoughtful, quiet voice.

3. **Stage a "tableau," a frozen moment of the poem posed as a "scene," with student volunteers posing** as described in the lines of the poem. Photograph and/or film the tableau and post it with the poem.

4. **In this lyrical poem, the poet explores emotions** and asks thoughtful questions. Guide students in identifying which lines suggest how the poet feels in this poem (such as *I think about them / Who they are / What they love*). What emotions does the poem evoke in us?

5. Follow up with another thoughtful poem by **Amy Ludwig VanDerwater, "Vacation"** (1st Grade, Week 36, page 102), or selections from *Amazing Faces*, edited by Lee Bennett Hopkins.

Take 5!

1. What is the perfect prop for this poem? A penny, of course. **Put a penny on the floor, read the poem aloud, and pick the penny up when you reach the final line.**

2. Read the poem aloud again and **invite students to BE the penny,** speaking the lines attributed to the penny: *"I'm your good luck ticket: / quick, pick me up!"* while you read the rest of the poem.

3. For discussion: **What is your favorite lucky token or item?**

4. Poets give their poems shape in many ways. Talk with students about each stanza, including the one-line stanza at the end, and what it adds to the poem. **Consider the poet's use of rhyme (eye/by; ticket/pick it) and dialogue, too.**

5. Pair this with another poem by **Constance Levy, "Bird Alert: Storm Warning!"** (4th Grade, Week 8, page 194), or poems from *Knock on Wood: Poems about Superstitions* by Janet Wong.

LUCKY PENNY
by **Constance Levy**

Any penny
I spy on the ground
beckons me
like the wink
of an eye.

I never say "Penny,
you won't make me rich"
and pass it by.

When it whispers to me:
*"I'm your good luck ticket;
quick, pick me up!"*

then UP I pick it!

LITTLE VILLAGE
by **Terry Webb Harshman**

Little village tucked
   in snow,
how I thrill to see
   your glow!
I plug your tiny
   street lamps in,
and, for a moment,
   I pretend . . .

that I am small . . .
I am there . . .
strolling in your busy square,
where I know every face by name . . .
every shop and windowpane.

Holidays are not
   as bright
Without the magic
   of your light.

Take 5!

1. **Encourage students to close their eyes and imagine a miniature village** with tiny buildings and tiny windows and tiny street lamps. Then continue by reading this poem aloud in a quiet voice.

2. In sharing the poem aloud again, display the text of the poem and **invite students to read the second stanza** while you read the rest aloud.

3. For discussion: *If you could visit a miniature place, where would you go and what would it be like?*

4. Lead students in identifying the pattern of rhyming words in this descriptive poem. The rhyme is usually found at the end of alternating lines, but the poet staggers the line breaks a bit in the second stanza. **Talk about the poet's use of "slant" rhyme or "almost" rhyme** in *in/pretend* and *name/windowpane* (where the rhyme depends on the final syllable).

5. Pair this poem with **George Ella Lyon's holiday poem, "Christmas Is"** (2nd Grade, Week 16, page 122), or selections from the e-book *Gift Tag*, edited by Sylvia Vardell and Janet Wong.

Take 5!

1. **Read this poem aloud with a bit of exasperation** while pantomiming motions of drying a dish with a dishtowel.

2. **Invite five volunteers to provide sound effects** while you read the poem aloud again, one each to shout, laugh, bark, stomp, and mock-cry. The first begins shouting when you read line 4 (*My grandpa shouts*) and continues until the end of the poem. Add the second volunteer laughing when you read line 7 (*Nobody laughs bigger than my dad*) and he/she keeps laughing. Add the barking in line 8, the stomping in line 9, and the (mock) crying in line 10, with ALL the sounds continuing until the end.

3. For discussion: *What are your family gatherings like?*

4. Guide students in seeing how the lines add characters and actions to build a story within the poem. **Can you picture the scene?**

5. Connect this poem with **"Double the Trouble" by Janet Wong** (2nd Grade, Week 13, page 119).

MY NOISY FAMILY
by **Michael Salinger**

When my family gets together
It can be very loud
Even when he's not mad
My grandpa shouts
The TV's always going in the next room
I can never be heard in this crowd
Nobody laughs bigger than dad
And the dog is barking 'cause he wants out
My big brother stomps his feet boom boom boom
And my baby sister cries louder than thunder
My grandma and I—we just wonder
Who's going to do the dishes?

CATCHING A YAWN
by **Avis Harley**

Why is it I'm always drawn
into someone else's yawn?

Every time I see the shape
of open mouth in cave-like gape
I feel the need to do the same,
as if it's some contagious game.

Perhaps it's empathy that stirs
when someone else's yawn occurs.

But even seeing the word in print
will send my brain the strongest hint
that I must yawn. And so I do.
Did reading this make you yawn, too?

Take 5!

1. What do you do while reading this poem aloud? **Yawn, of course, and repeatedly throughout the poem.** You may need to explain a few words like *gape, contagious*, and *empathy*.

2. Read the poem aloud again, but this time **involve students in reading the opening question** in the first two lines and then yawning repeatedly while you read the rest aloud.

3. Sometimes poets weave facts into their poems. **Guide students in noting what information we learn about yawns and yawning** in this poem.

4. Talk with students about each stanza in this poem and how **the poet alternates two-line stanzas** (*couplets*) **with four-line stanzas** (*quatrains*) while maintaining the rhyme scheme with every two lines rhyming. Lead students in identifying each pair of rhyming words, too (*drawn/yawn; shape/gape; same/game; stirs/occurs; print/hint; do/too*).

5. Follow up with another poem by **Avis Harley, "Recess"** (2nd Grade, Week 2, page 108).

IT'S A WRAP
by **Carol-Ann Hoyte**

Take 5!

1. **Read this poem aloud, and ask students to guess what this poem is about. If needed, point out clue words such as** *cut, scratch, bruise, bump.*

2. For a follow-up reading, **invite students to finish the poem by reading the last two lines** (*do not despair / 'cause I self repair*) while you read the rest aloud. You may need to explain the word *despair.*

3. Use this teachable moment to **talk about basic first aid and how to handle simple cuts, scratches, bruises, and bumps.**

4. **This poem is an example of a riddle poem. Guide students in identifying the clues that suggest the poem's subject.** Then talk about how the lines are arranged, with words even broken up (like *lay- / ered*) to dole out the facts bit by bit, and how only the final two lines rhyme.

5. Link this poem with another riddle poem by **Carol-Ann Hoyte, "From Root to Tip"** (5th Grade, Week 19, page 245).

I'm the
three
  lay-
    ered
waterproof wrapping
which warms you up
and cools you down;
but if you cut, scratch,
bruise, or bump me
do not despair
'cause I self repair.

Answer: skin

HOW THE BIRDS GOT THEIR COLORS
by Joseph Bruchac

Long ago, it is said,
all the birds were brown.
Gluskonba loved the red and gold
and all the other colors
the trees turned every autumn.

But he grew sad
when winter came
and all those leaves
fell from the trees.

So Gluskonba bent down
and picked up all those
colors from the ground.

He gave those colors
to the birds
so he could see them
all year round.

Take 5!

1. Point out to students that **many poems are funny, but some are quiet and thoughtful**—like this one based on a Native American legend from the Abenaki people. You may also need to provide background on *Gluskonba,* known as "the one who helps the people."

2. Share the poem again, **inviting students to echo read the lines of the second stanza only**, repeating each line after you say it. Then you read the rest of the poem aloud.

3. For discussion: *What are your favorite colors of fall?*

4. **This poem is an example of a narrative poem—a poem that tells a story.** Guide students in seeing how the stanzas build to create this poem story. Talk about how the poet uses some rhyme (*leaves/ trees; brown/down/ground/ round*), but not always in a regular pattern.

5. Pair this with another poem about Gluskonba and the birds by **Joseph Bruchac, "How the Geese Became Chiefs of the Birds"** (5th Grade, Week 8, page 234).

THE DO KIND
by Janet Wong

Take 5!

1. Before sharing this poem (in a soft voice), point out to students that **many poems are humorous, but some are serious—like this one.**

2. Read the poem aloud again, and this time **invite students to chime in on the words *me me me* in line 6 and *me and you* in line 8.** Cue students by pointing to your ear.

3. For discussion: *What makes a friend special to you?*

4. **Poems usually rhyme at the end of lines, but sometimes they rhyme in the middle too, which is called *internal rhyme*.** Challenge the students to find the internal rhyming words in the lines of this poem (*see/me; do/you*).

5. Link this poem with another poem about friendship by **Janet Wong, "Forgive and Forget"** (2nd Grade, Week 22, page 128), and with selections from *The Friendly Four* by Eloise Greenfield.

When my ball flies over the wall,
you run and get it back.

When my books fall down the stairs,
you help me pick them up.

Some friends are *see* friends,
me me me friends.

You are the *do* kind,
the *me and you* kind.

SMALL TALK
by **Ken Slesarik**

He speaks and thinks that he endears
but only talks and never hears.

On and on he blabs, it's endless.
You'd think that it would leave him friendless.

Alone with others, there he dwells,
with those who like to hear themselves.

Take 5!

1. **Introduce a few key words essential to understanding the poem**, like *endears, blabs, friendless,* and *dwells.*

2. If possible, display the text of the poem and **ask students to read the second line of each stanza** as you read the first line of each stanza.

3. **Talk with students about how it feels to be around someone who is always talking and never listens.**

4. Help students find the rhyming pairs of words that occur at the end of each stanza (*endears/hears; endless/friendless; dwells/ themselves*). **Note the "almost" or "slant" rhyme in** *dwells/themselves.* Then read the poem aloud again, emphasizing the rhyming words in particular.

5. Follow up by sharing the poem **"Embarrassed" by Jacqueline Jules** (1st Grade, Week 22, page 88).

Take 5!

1. While reading this poem aloud, **play a clip of a nature scene** with sound effects from Calm.com. Look for a mountain or river scene to fit the poem.

2. For a second reading, **invite students to echo read the first and last stanzas of the poem as if echoing from a mountain top.** They repeat each line after you read it aloud.

3. For discussion: *If you could go anywhere in the world to explore for a week, where would you go?*

4. In this lyrical poem, the poet speculates on what makes us want to explore the world, what keeps us wondering and wandering. **Guide students in discussing which lines suggest how the poet feels in this poem** (such as *yearn to go; need to know more*). What emotions does the poem evoke?

5. Share another poem about exploring, **"Give Me Wings" by Graham Denton** (4th Grade, Week 23, page 209).

EXPLORER
by **Joan Bransfield Graham**

The chill call
of mountain peak
speaks to those
who climb and seek
to touch the sky.

The winding way
of river's flow
lures those who
yearn to go
where none
have gone before.

Ancient as earth,
a need to know more,
to answer the questions—
reach out, EXPLORE!

VACATION COMMUNICATION
by Carol-Ann Hoyte

Don't go, I'll miss you too much
Promise you will stay in touch
I-M, fax, email, or text
to tell me when I'll see you next
Or just send a letter, Matt
'Scuse me, what on earth is that?

Take 5!

1. Use your cell phone (if you have one) as a poetry prop and **pretend you are texting** while you read this poem aloud slowly.

2. Share the poem aloud again, and this time **invite students to join in on the final line** (*'Scuse me, what on earth is that?).

3. **Talk with students about the purpose and format for letter writing**. Then write one as a class (to a former student who has moved, a class parent, the mayor, etc.) and mail it!

4. This poem is another good example of humorous poetry. **Talk with students about how the poet creates humor in this poem through the surprise of the final line.** It can also be sung to the tune of "Twinkle, Twinkle, Little Star."

5. Revisit the first poem of the year, **"Funday, Imaginary 1st" by Heidi Mordhorst** (3rd Grade, Week 1, page 147), for a poem in the form of a letter.

Take 5!

1. Read this poem aloud while **pantomiming the many action words in the poem,** such as dreaming, leaping, bowing, posing, spinning, nose-wrinkling, and knee-wobbling. You may need to explain the word *pirouette*.

2. Share the poem again and **invite eight or more student volunteers to take on the roles** of Gracie the "Cowlerina" (the cow), Madame Goose, duck(s), cat, rabbit(s), chicken(s), goose, and bull.

3. **Talk with students about a pet performance they might imagine at home or an animal ballet at the zoo.**

4. Sometimes poets use words that mimic sounds, which is called *onomatopoeia*. **Challenge the students to see how many sound words they can find** in this poem (such as *squawk, thud, thump, moo, cluck, cackle, hiss, boo, whoosh*). Then read this narrative poem aloud again, emphasizing the sound words.

5. Share **"Animal Talk" by Charles Ghigna** (Kindergarten, Week 27, page 53).

BARNYARD BALLET
by **Jeannine Atkins**

No one claps after the morning
milking, or cheers for a grazing cow.
So Gracie dreams of tutus, dancing,
leaping, and taking a bow.

Madame Goose squawks "Pirouette!"
The ducks strike elegant poses.
The cat silently spins.
Rabbits point up their pink noses.

Gracie's four knees wobble. Instead
of twirling, she thuds, thumps, and moos.
The chickens cluck and cackle.
The goose hisses. A bull boos.

Must Gracie go back to the clover?
Did she try to twirl too soon?
She points her hooves, swishes her tail.
Whoosh! Cowlerina leaps over the mooooon!

EIGHT-YEAR-OLD UNCLE
by **X.J. Kennedy**

In school they call me Uncle Moe
    Though all I am is eight.
My sister is a mother now.
    Did I get born too late?

The other kids say, "Hey, you're old!"
    They won't leave me in peace,
But somehow I don't want to scold
    My brand new baby niece..

Take 5!

1. Read this poem aloud and be prepared to **explain how an eight-year-old child can already have a niece** (if he has an older adult sister with a child).

2. In a follow-up reading, **invite students to say the sentence in quotation marks,** *"Hey, you're old!"* while you read the rest of the poem.

3. **Talk with students about how families can include all kinds of people.**

4. Talk with students about how the poet creates humor in this poem in nearly every line. **Pinpoint examples in the words, phrases, and ideas the poet uses,** such as: a child who is called "Uncle," a sister who is a mother, the possibility of being born late, what other kids say, and scolding a baby. For even more humorous effect, sing this poem to the tune of "99 Bottles of Pop."

5. Connect this poem with others by **X. J. Kennedy** like **"Bat"** (1st Grade, Week 8, page 74) or **"Armadillo"** (1st Grade, Week 26, page 92).

Take 5!

1. Hold a dictionary open, as if searching for a word, while you read this poem aloud. Or **open an online dictionary and project an entry** (for *maggots*, perhaps) while you share the poem.

2. Invite the students to say the italicized words in the poem (*hospital, lost, maggots,* etc.). This may also be the perfect opportunity to look up unfamiliar words and **demonstrate dictionary research skills, too.**

3. For discussion: *What are some of your favorite words?*

4. Talk with students about how the poet uses two-line stanzas (couplets) with ending words rhyming in every two stanzas (*uneasy/queasy; splashes/ashes; ball/all*). **Consider why the poet chose two-line stanzas instead of four-line stanzas** (possibly because the meanings of the words in each stanza are related).

5. Connect this poem with one about spellchecking, **"Spanish Ears" by Carmen T. Bernier-Grand** (2nd Grade, Week 27, page 133).

LOOK IT UP!
by **Heidi Bee Roemer**

Hospital and *lost* are words
that make me feel uneasy.

Maggots, germs, and *brussels sprouts*
make my tummy queasy.

Words like *pool* and *water slide*
are filled with splishy splashes.

Tent and toasted *marshmallows*
spark thoughts of glowing ashes.

Words that make me stomp and cheer
are *home run, bat* and *ball;*

But *dictionary* is my most
favorite word of all!

A QUIET DAY
by **Amy Ludwig VanDerwater**

A quiet day is like a park.
You can be alone.
You can play hide-and-seek inside your brain.
You can remember everything you ever did.
You can dream.
You can draw a picture.
You can be you
sitting in the sunshine
thinking thoughts on your own bench
watching squirrels run around in your head.
You can even bring a book.

Take 5!

1. This is **a quiet poem to read in a quiet voice with pauses** at the end of each line.

2. Read the poem again, **inviting students to say the repeated words** *You can* at the beginning of many lines.

3. For discussion: ***What do you like to do when you are alone?***

4. This is a lyrical poem that considers different ways to spend a quiet day. What thoughts or emotions does the poem prompt in us? **Lead students in considering how repeating key words and phrases (like *You can*) helps build a poem** and can add to the distinctive rhythm of the lines.

5. Follow up with another thoughtful poem about the power of imagination by **Amy Ludwig VanDerwater, "Vacation"** (1st Grade, Week 36, page 102).

Take 5!

1. Tuck a copy of this poem into a can and label it "A POEM CAN." Show the can before taking the poem out and reading it. **Challenge students to listen for the phrase *a poem can* as** you read the poem aloud.

2. Then follow up by **inviting students to say the words *A poem can*** as you read the rest of the poem aloud. You also may want to explain the pun or double meaning in using the phrase *a poem can* two ways.

3. Talk with students about any **poems they have read or heard that were *cozy* or *scary like the night.***

4. Discuss with students how poets can create poems in many different ways. Here **the poet combines several features in the poem**: the repetition of key words (*Like the...; a poem can*), the four-line stanza, and a lyrical description in each stanza in the form of a simile. Yet, the poem does not rhyme. Then read the poem aloud together once again.

5. Connect this poem with another one about poems, **"Recipe for a Poem" by Kristy Dempsey** (2nd Grade, Week 29, page 135).

POEM LIKE THE SEA
by Patricia Hubbell

Like the sea
A poem
Can be
Wild and wavy
Or smooth and calm

Like a pond
A poem
Can hold
Shimmering
Reflections

Like the night
A poem
Can be
Cozy or scary

Like the moon
A poem
Can be
Mysterious and glowing

Like the stars
A poem
Can
Glitter and shine

Like the morning sun
A poem
Can
Blaze you awake

THE WRITER'S DRILL
by **Esther Hershenhorn**

Place pen in hand, ready paper and repeat:

I don't know but I been told
Question Words nail stories cold.
Stuck mid-sentence, lost your WOW?
Try *Who? What? Why?*
Then *When? Where? How?*

Write on! One, two.
Write on! Three, four.
Write on! Five, six, seven, eight, nine, ten
Until The End!

Take 5!

1. Add pantomime to this poem as you read it aloud, **holding a pen and piece of paper as if you are ready to write.**

2. **Do you recognize the cadence of the drill sergeant's marching chant here?** This poem is ideal for chanting with an echoing of lines. It may take some practice to get the rhythm right, but have fun with it.

3. For discussion: *What is the hardest part about writing?*

4. Point out that sometimes poets borrow the patterns from other things, like songs and chants, to create a new poem. Here, **the poet takes a military chant and turns it into a poem.** Talk with students about how the words, lines, and stanzas are broken up and arranged on the page.

5. Compare this with another poem with a military connection, **"Skype" by Janet Wong** (1st Grade, Week 24, page 90).

CATKU
by **Lee Wardlaw**

Cat instruction book:
Nap, play, bathe, nap, eat, repeat.
Practice makes perfect.

Feline in distress!
Evil couch caught catnip mouse!
You to the rescue.

Stranger coos: *"Itty
pwetty kitty!"* A fur ball
serves as my reply.

Take 5!

1. Point out the clever play on words in the title: *Catku* **= haiku poems about cats.** Then read the poems aloud in a kitty cat voice to convey the cat's point of view.

2. Share the poems again, inviting students to say the quote in italics in the third stanza, *"Itty pwetty kitty!"* **with exaggerated sweetness.**

3. For discussion: *If these are the elements of the "cat instruction book," what might a "dog instruction book" include?*

4. **This is an example of a poem form that usually does not rhyme, a haiku poem.** Originally a Japanese form of poetry, a haiku focuses on nature in only three lines (generally 5 syllables, 7 syllables, 5 syllables). Guide students in understanding the haiku form with these examples.

5. Follow up with another descriptive cat poem, **"All Worn Out" by Kristy Dempsey** (2nd Grade, Week 5, page 111), and with Lee Wardlaw's haiku picture book, *Won Ton: A Cat Tale Told in Haiku.*

HONEY
by **J. Patrick Lewis**

A busy bee's a poem
With nectar that's so fine
A reader-eater laps up every
Honey of a line.

Take 5!

1. **Encourage students to close their eyes and imagine a bee flying,** buzzing, stopping on a flower, and so on. Then continue by reading this poem aloud.

2. Read the poem again, **inviting students to say the phrase *reader-eater*** while you read the rest.

3. **Talk with students about how sometimes poets make up words (like *reader-eater*)** to make their poems even more interesting.

4. **Poets compare one thing to another to give us a fresh perspective on both things.** Lead the students in talking about how bees and poems are alike in this poem. Use examples from the poem (nectar is fine, poem lines are like honey).

5. Look for other poems about insects by **J. Patrick Lewis** such as **"Gnat and Flea"** (1st Grade, Week 27, page 93), or selections from *Unbeelievables: Honeybee Poems and Paintings* by Douglas Florian.

Take 5!

1. Have a stapler handy. **As you read the poem, show the stapler and staple through paper.** Show the stapler at the end of the poem.

2. Next, **invite students to echo read the beginning of the poem,** repeating the first four words/ lines emphatically after you read each one aloud. Then read the rest of the poem aloud.

3. For discussion: *If a stapler is like a bulldog, what are pencils, scissors, or paper clips like?*

4. Sometimes poets use their imaginations to guess what it might be like if something that is not alive had a real personality. This technique is called *personification*. Guide the students in determining **which words or lines in this poem suggest a stapler is a breathing being** (*crunches, sinking teeth, leaving / a silver scar*).

5. Share another poem by **Georgia Heard, "The Winner"** (2nd Grade, Week 3, page 109), or selections from the poetry book she edited, *Falling Down the Page: A Book of List Poems.*

STAPLER
by **Georgia Heard**

Bulldog

crunches

down
hard

sinking

teeth
into paper—

leaving
a silver scar.

CAR TRIP
by Juanita Havill

"Nine hundred miles to Miami,"
Mom says as she starts the car.

We take our games and books and snacks
whenever we travel far.

"How many miles to Your Ami?"
I squeal at the first stop sign.

"Nine hundred minus one," says Mom,
"makes eight hundred ninety-nine."

Take 5!

1. Have a map of Florida as a poetry prop. Then **show Miami on the map and talk about the child's misunderstanding about the word** (Miami = My Ami).

2. The dialogue in this poem lends itself to reading in two parts. **Invite the students to read the child's comments in lines 1 and 5** while you read the rest aloud.

3. **Take a moment to talk about car trips** that students have experienced.

4. This is a poem with two voices or characters. **Point out** quotation marks and dialogue. Then consider how the ending rhymes (*car/far; sign/nine*) help make what could be simply dialogue a rhyming poem.

5. Connect this poem with others containing dialogue, such as **"I Might Go to Mars," also by Juanita Havill** (2nd Grade, Week 28, page 134).

Take 5!

1. Feeling brave? **You can sing this poem to the tune of "On Top of Old Smoky."** You may also need to explain the word *dismay* to students.

2. This time, read the poem aloud while displaying the words of the poem, if possible. **Invite students to chime in on the last two lines of the poem**—the surprise twist at the end (*Good thing her vacation / is only a week*).

3. For discussion: *How can you keep in touch with friends when you're apart?*

4. This poem is another good example of humorous poetry. **Talk with students about how the poet creates humor in this poem through the surprise twist at the end, confounding the expectation of the title** and the long list of worries.

5. Share another funny poem about friendship with a surprise twist at the end with **"Greetings" by Leslea Newman** (5th Grade, Week 17, page 243).

MY BEST FRIEND IS LEAVING
by **Debbie Levy**

My best friend is leaving.
I'm crushed, I'm dismayed.
I'm crabby, I'm crusty,
and yes—I'm afraid.

I'm afraid she'll forget me,
afraid that she might
find a better best friend
and I'll fade out of sight.

We promise to write
twice a day, maybe more.
But what of the time in between?
What a bore.

My best friend is leaving.
My summer looks bleak. . . .
Good thing her vacation
is only a week.

MOON BUGGY
by **Juanita Havill**

When we landed, it was quiet here.
No noisy traffic.
No chattering crowds.
No cities.

No tractors plowing.
No moo or bray or cock-a-doodle-do.
No farms.

We were the first to shatter the silence,
and whoever comes
in a hundred years
will see our footprints
and the paths we traced in barren dust
with our moon buggy.

Take 5!

1. **Project an image of the moon in the background** while you read this poem out loud with a quiet voice.

2. Read the poem again and **ask for six volunteers**, one to read each line beginning with *No (No noisy traffic; No chattering crowds; No cities; No tractors plowing; No moo or bray or cock-a-doodle-do; No farms)* while you read the remainder of the poem aloud.

3. For discussion: ***What would it be like to travel to the moon or outer space?***

4. Sometimes poets weave facts into their poems. **Guide students in noting what information we learn about the first moon landing in this poem.** Talk about how writers can share information in many formats, including poems and paragraphs.

5. Share another fact-filled poem written by **Juanita Havill, "Wheel of Progress"** (5th Grade, Week 24, page 250), or selections from *A Burst of Firsts* by J. Patrick Lewis.

POEMS FOR FOURTH GRADE

Common Core Standards
for Fourth Grade (RL.4.2; RL.4.5)

In sharing poetry with fourth graders, we can support their expanding vocabularies, promote a playful interaction with words and language, and develop their confidence in comprehending text.

First we focus on enjoyment and understanding, and then we guide students in responding to poetry in various forms and articulating themes from key ideas and details in the poems.

In sharing poetry aloud and in print, we can guide students in understanding how structural elements like verse, rhythm, and meter help shape a poem.

In fun and participatory ways, we can celebrate poetry while gently introducing and reinforcing key skills.

week 1	School	Feeling Jumpy *by Patricia Hubbell*
week 2	More School	Fifty Yard Dash *by Lorie Ann Grover*
week 3	Fun & Games	Running Back *by Jacqueline Jules*
week 4	Pets	My Porcupine Is Feeling Fine *by Kenn Nesbitt*
week 5	More Pets	Pirate Parrot *by Julie Larios*
week 6	On the Ground	The Ostrich *by Linda Ashman*
week 7	In the Water	Humpback Whale *by Jane Yolen*
week 8	In the Air	Bird Alert: Storm Warning! *by Constance Levy*
week 9	Weather	When the Rain Falls *by Susan Taylor Brown*
week 10	Food	Global Gorging *by Terry Webb Harshman*
week 11	More Food	Avocado *by Constance Levy*
week 12	House & Home	The Front Yard Where the Maple Tree Stands *by Allan Wolf*
week 13	Families	The Way You Sound *by John Grandits*
week 14	Community	Saturdays *by Monica Gunning*
week 15	Stuff We Love	Riddle *by Nikki Grimes*
week 16	Holidays	Gift Ungiven *by JonArno Lawson*
week 17	Time Together	Bailes *by Guadalupe Garcia McCall*
week 18	Human Body	I Had to Get a Shot at the Doctor's *by April Halprin Wayland*
week 19	More Human Body	The Guy in the Closet *by Heidi Bee Roemer*
week 20	Art & Colors	I've Never Seen a Purple Cow *by Lesléa Newman*
week 21	Love & Friendship	A Branch of Friendship *by Avis Harley*
week 22	A Kinder Place	Poem for a Bully *by Eileen Spinelli*
week 23	Exploring	Give Me Wings *by Graham Denton*
week 24	Science & Tech	Super Key Man *by Esther Hershenhorn*
week 25	Song & Dance	You Think This Is A Dance *by Arnold Adoff*
week 26	Nonsense	Why Hippos Look Baked *by J. Patrick Lewis*
week 27	World of Words	The Elders Told Me *by Joseph Bruchac*
week 28	Books	Archeology of a Book *by Betsy Franco*
week 29	Poetry Poems	Today *by Eileen Spinelli*
week 30	RR&R	The Kangarooster *by Jack Prelutsky*
week 31	Different Forms	Corn, Before the Butter *by Laura Purdie Salas*
week 32	Metaphor & Simile	Crocodile *by Deborah Chandra*
week 33	Personification	Summer Storm *by Irene Latham*
week 34	On the Move	Crossing the International Date Line *by Joan Bransfield Graham*
week 35	Summer Vacation	Family Vacation *by Kathi Appelt*
week 36	Looking Forward	Centipede *by Michael J. Rosen*

*"Think about how you feel when you read a poem that really speaks to you, one that perfectly expresses what you're thinking and feeling. When you read that, you feel understood, right? I know I do. You feel less alone. I know I do. You realize **despite all our differences, there are so many human experiences and emotions that we share."***

୫ଡ଼ Michelle Obama ଡ଼୫

Take 5!

1. To add some drama to reading this poem aloud, **show a test answer sheet and bubble in responses as you read** the final stanza. You can find printable examples at teachervision.fen.com.

2. Next, **invite students to join in reading the poem aloud by saying the words *Tick tock* (four times) in the last stanza. Cue them by raising your pencil.**

3. For discussion: ***How do you feel when it's time to take a test?***

4. Poems usually rhyme at the end of lines, but sometimes they rhyme in the middle too, which is called *internal rhyme*. Challenge the students to find the pairs of words that rhyme at the end of lines (*jumpy/ grumpy; stick-lumpy/jumpy; hand/ stand; done/run*) as well as rhymes in the middle of lines (*test-time/rest time*). **There is an "almost" or "slant" end rhyme (*tock/dot*) that students may also notice.**

5. Follow up with other poems about test-taking, **"The World's Most Intelligent Chicken" by Jack Prelutsky** (5th Grade, Week 1, page 227) or **"Backpack" by Irene Latham** (5th Grade, Week 2, page 228), or selections from *School Fever* by Brod Bagert.

FEELING JUMPY
by Patricia Hubbell

I'm feeling jittery jumpy
I'm growly and I'm grumpy
My brain's all sticky-lumpy
I'm take-a-test-time jumpy

Test-time's not my best time
It's my nervy not-at-rest time

Pencil in my hand
It's time to take a stand

Tick tock
Fill in a dot
Tick tock
Fill in a dot
Tick tock
Fill in a dot
Tick tock—
DONE!

"Let's all . . . RUN!"

FIFTY YARD DASH
by **Lorie Ann Grover**

Feet thump. Left, right, left.
Arms punch. Breath bursts. In, out, in.
Flying on the run.

Take 5!

1. Read this poem aloud while pantomiming or running in place, or **invite a student to run in place beside you while you read** the poem aloud.

2. Share the poem aloud again, **inviting students to chime in** on the words *Left, right, left* and *In, out, in.* Cue students by pointing to your ear.

3. For discussion: **Which do you enjoy more, playing sports or watching sports?**

4. Many poems rhyme, but not all. **This is an example of a poem form that usually does not rhyme, a haiku poem.** Originally a Japanese form of poetry, a haiku focuses on nature in only three lines (generally 5 syllables, 7 syllables, 5 syllables). Guide students in understanding the haiku form with this example.

5. Connect this poem with more sports-themed haiku poems such as **"Equipment Haiku" by Jen Bryant** (5th Grade, Week 3, page 229), or with examples of the sijo poem form in *Tap Dancing on the Roof* by Linda Sue Park.

Take 5!

1. Before reading this poem, **play a video clip of a football game** (without sound) to set the stage, or play it as a background while you read the poem aloud.

2. Read the poem aloud again while displaying the words of the poem, if possible. **Invite students to join in on lines 9, 10, and 11** *(I watch from my living room, / sometimes booing, / sometimes cheering)*; urge them to boo after line 19 and cheer after line 11.

3. To follow up, **students can talk about their favorite sports teams** (football or other sport, professional or school team).

4. Discuss with students how many poems rhyme, but not all. **This poem is an example of** *free verse*. It doesn't rhyme, but guide students in seeing how the lines and line breaks build to create a poem. Challenge them to summarize what the poem is about in a nutshell.

5. Pair this poem with **"Watching Football" by Janet Wong** (1st Grade, Week 17, page 83), or selections from *And the Crowd Goes Wild!: A Global Gathering of Sports Poems* edited by Carol-Ann Hoyte and Heidi Bee Roemer.

RUNNING BACK
by **Jacqueline Jules**

He's on the big screen again,
with padded shoulders,
and shiny tight pants.
The number on his jersey
identifies him clearly
for the cameras and the crowd,
as he clamps a strap under his chin,
without ever looking up.
I watch from my living room,
sometimes booing,
sometimes cheering,
but always wishing
I could put on a helmet
and run like that—
past all those guys
trying to knock me down—
not caring a bit
who's booing or who's cheering,
'cause I've got the ball in my hand.

MY PORCUPINE IS FEELING FINE
by **Kenn Nesbitt**

My porcupine is feeling fine,
but what an unexpected twist!
He used to be my cat before
he saw the acupuncturist.

Take 5!

1. **Be sure students are familiar with porcupines** before reading this poem aloud. You may wish to display a picture. Pause dramatically before the last two words (*the acupuncturist*).

2. Read the poem aloud again, and this time **invite the students to read the last two words aloud** (*the acupuncturist*). Practice pronouncing the word—and explain it—if needed. Cue students by raising a pointer or pencil.

3. **Invite students to share their own funny pet stories.**

4. This poem is an example of humorous poetry. **Why is this funny? Ask the students! Responses will vary,** but might include: the surprise ending, the image of a cat looking like a porcupine, the cat visiting an acupuncturist, the word *acupuncturist,* and so on.

5. Connect this poem with another about a porcupine pet, **"Oh Man!" by David L. Harrison** (Kindergarten, Week 5, page 31), or others by Kenn Nesbitt in *The Tighty Whitey Spider: And More Wacky Animal Poems I Totally Made Up.*

PIRATE PARROT
by **Julie Larios**

I dressed my bird in pantaloons,
a puffy shirt,
a pirate hat.

I taped a toothpick dagger to
his little beak—
he squawked at that.

I trained him to say "YARR!" and then
he walked the plank—
and that was that.

Take 5!

1. Set the stage for this poem by encouraging students to close their eyes and imagine a classic pirate scene complete with squawking parrot. Then **read this poem aloud and be prepared to squawk.**

2. Share the poem again, but this time **invite students to say the parrot line in the poem, *"YARR!"***

3. **Talk with students about some of their favorite experiences with costumes, drama, or theater.**

4. **Poets often use words that mimic sounds in their writing (called *onomatopoeia*).** Sometimes they use one word to describe making a sound (such as *squawk*) and another word to describe a sound itself (*YARR*). Think of the things that could be described as pirate sounds. What words could you use to describe those sounds?

5. For another humorous poem about a clothing-wearing animal, look for **"A Centipede's Excuse" by Kristy Dempsey** (1st Grade, Week 34, page 100), or for more pirate-themed poems, look for *Pirates* by David L. Harrison.

THE OSTRICH
by Linda Ashman

His little wings
are feeble things:
his flying is a bust.

But run top speed,
it's guaranteed—
he'll leave you in the dust.

Note: The ostrich is the fastest two-legged animal, reaching speeds of 45 miles per hour.

Take 5!

1. **Provide helpful context by showing a short video clip** (without sound) of an ostrich running as you read the poem aloud. One possibility: youtube.com/watch?v=rhpVgUCHDIE.

2. Next, display the words of the poem, if possible, and **invite students to echo read selected lines from the poem**, repeating lines 1 and 2 (*His little wings / are feeble things*) and lines 4 and 5 (*But run top speed / it's guaranteed*) after you read each line aloud.

3. Sometimes poets weave facts into their poems. **Guide students in noting what information we learn about ostriches** in this poem.

4. Poets give their poems shape in many ways. **Talk with students about each stanza and what it adds to the poem** (one shares the ostrich's weaknesses, one shares strengths). Consider the poet's use of rhyme, too (*wings/things; speed/ guaranteed; bust/dust*), noting that the rhyming pair of *speed* and *guaranteed* depends on the final syllable of *guaranteed*.

5. For another fact-filled animal poem, share **"The Star-Nosed Mole" by Leslie Bulion** (2nd Grade, Week 7, page 113), or selections from *A Whiff of Pine, A Hint of Skunk* by Deborah Ruddell.

Take 5!

1. **Share a National Geographic video of humpback whales** without sound while reading the poem aloud. Videos can be found at Video.NationalGeographic.com.

2. Read the poem aloud while displaying the text, with **students participating in reading four key lines aloud**—lines 1 and 2 (*If a whale could fly / it would be the humpback*) and lines 5 and 6 (*If a whale had wings / it would be the humpback*)— while you read the rest.

3. **Discuss any unfamiliar words** such as *humpback, fluke, tonnage, breach*. Highlight the poet's use of the made-up word *bird-sphere*. Poets like to do that!

4. **This poem is another example of free verse.** It doesn't rhyme, but guide students in seeing how the poem still has a rhythm with some repetition (*If a whale. . . / it would be the humpback*). Also discuss how the poet incorporates factual information about the whale into the poem, and challenge students to identify some of those details.

5. For another example of this poet's writing, look for **Jane Yolen's poem "Pumpkin"** (3rd Grade, Week 11, page 157), or for ocean-related poems, seek out selections from *Water Sings Blue: Ocean Poems* by Kate Coombs.

HUMPBACK WHALE
by **Jane Yolen**

If a whale could fly
it would be the humpback,
flinging itself out of the bright waves,
heaving itself into the bird-sphere.
If a whale had wings
it would be the humpback,
flukes feathering fast
to lift its tonnage
out of the breach
into the lightening air.

BIRD ALERT: STORM WARNING!
by **Constance Levy**

Quick—
to a tree
or under the eaves!

Rush
to a bush,
where the leaves
are thick!

Hurry and hide
till the storm
subsides!

Start dashing—
don't wait
until the last
minute—
wet winds will be lashing
and you'll be in it!

Don't stop . . .
I repeat: DON'T STOP
to go splashing!

Take 5!

1. **Read this poem aloud while moving around the room pantomiming** some of the bird motions suggested in the poem (standing under something tall, rushing to another spot, hiding in another place, dashing to another spot, pretending to splash in a puddle).

2. Share the poem again, displaying the text, if possible, and **invite students to say the first line of each stanza with you** (*Quick; Rush; Hurry and hide; Start dashing; Don't stop*).

3. For discussion: ***What do you do to feel safe during a storm?***

4. Talk with students about each stanza and what it adds to the poem. **Consider the poet's use and placement of end rhymes and "almost" or "slant" rhymes** (*tree/eaves/leaves; Rush/bush; hide/subsides; dashing/lashing/splashing; minute/in it*) and of all capital letters, too (*DON'T STOP*).

5. Follow up with another poem about what to do in a storm, **"Stormy Day" by Rebecca Kai Dotlich** (Kindergarten, Week 17, page 43).

WHEN THE RAIN FALLS
by **Susan Taylor Brown**

Clouds curl.
Thunder trembles.
Lightning leaps.
Coats cover.
Umbrellas unfold.
Wipers wave.
Rivers rise.
Buckets bail.
Puddles plash.
Mud melts.
Worms wiggle.
Rainbows reappear.

Take 5!

1. Read this poem aloud, pausing briefly at the end of each line for extra emphasis. **Talk with students about how poets like to make up words (like *plash*).**

2. Share the poem again, displaying the text of the poem, if possible, and **invite students to say three lines together** for greater volume and emphasis: line 2 (*Thunder trembles*), line 7 (*Rivers rise*), and line 12 (*Rainbows reappear*).

3. For discussion: *What are the best and worst things about a rainy day?*

4. Sometimes poets like to use many words that start the same (*alliteration*) to add to the sound of the poem. **Challenge students to notice the use of alliteration in EVERY line,** and talk about how the poet sequences the lines in a logical order. Read the poem aloud together again, inviting students to choose their favorite line and chime in when that line appears.

5. Link this poem with **"My Dog" by Charles Waters** (1st Grade, Week 9, page 75), or look for *All the Water in the World* by George Ella Lyon.

GLOBAL GORGING
by Terry Webb Harshman

New York bagels!
Scottish scones!
Warm, Italian
cheese calzones!

Irish soda bread
with stew!
Crusty French bread!
Croissants, too!

Chinese dumplings!
Egg rolls, noodles!
English muffins!
German strudels!

Seeded, twisted,
Flat or curled—
I'll eat my way
AROUND THE WORLD!

Take 5!

1. A poem about food is always more fun when you share food. **Bring a bagel, scone, or croissant** (or other poem menu item) to show and share after you read this poem aloud. Talk about any foods mentioned (mostly breads!) that might be unfamiliar to the students.

2. Read the poem aloud again, displaying the text, and **invite students to join in on the final two lines** (*I'll eat my way / AROUND THE WORLD*).

3. For discussion: *What are some of your favorite foods (from around the world)?*

4. Poets love to play with words and how they are arranged on the page. Here the poem is almost like a list and the short lines, four-line stanzas (or quatrains), and regular rhymes help you know how to read it. **Invite students to tap the rhythm of the poem** as you share it again. Like a composer with the notes of a song, poets give their poems a beat too.

5. Connect this poem with another global food poem, **"Grandfather's Chopsticks" by Janet Wong** (1st Grade, Week 11, page 77).

Take 5!

1. If possible, **bring an avocado as a poetry prop** to set the stage, and then read this poem aloud with a short pause between stanzas.

2. Share the poem aloud again, and **invite students to join in on the final line, *HAPPY GUACAMOLE!***

3. Here the poet presents descriptive directions that are almost like a recipe. **Talk with students about the steps they might use for making guacamole.**

4. Help students identify the rhyming words that occur in this poem— even within and across stanzas, including **"almost"** or **"slant"** rhymes (*all/all/small/ football; leather/butter; seed/ yellow-green; seed/need; butter/ better; thick/crisp/chip*). Display the poem, then read it aloud again, emphasizing all the rhyming words in particular.

5. Follow up with a related poem, **"A Taste of Taco" by Rebecca Kai Dotlich** (2nd Grade, Week 11, page 117), or the recipe poem book, *Guacamole: Un poema para cocinar/A Cooking Poem* by Jorge Argueta.

AVOCADO
by **Constance Levy**

All in all,
it's a small
football

covered in
alligator leather,

wrapped around
a round
slick seed
surrounded by
yellow-green butter.

Remove the seed;
it's the butter you'll need,
and to make it even better—

season it, mash it,
spread it thick
over a crisp tortilla chip

    and—

HAPPY GUACAMOLE!

THE FRONT YARD
WHERE THE MAPLE TREE STANDS
by Allan Wolf

The Maple tree in the front yard embraces
the children who climb her with green leafy hands.
Ask and I'll tell you my favorite place is
the front yard outside where the Maple tree stands.

It is there that the children begin the long races.
And there where they gather in innocent bands.
Whatever the game or adventure, home base is
the front yard outside where the Maple tree stands.

No matter what wonders and wide open spaces
I see when I travel to faraway lands.
If asked I'll still say my most favorite place is
the front yard outside where the Maple tree stands.

Take 5!

1. **Project the image of a tree** (preferably a maple tree with golden leaves) while reading this poem aloud. A source is Tree-Pictures.com.

2. Share the poem aloud again. **Invite students to join in on the final line of each stanza.**

3. For discussion: *What is your favorite outside place to be?*

4. This is a lyrical poem that reveals the poet thinking about a favorite place in the world. **Lead students in considering how repeating key words and phrases (like the final line in each stanza) helps build a poem** and can add to the distinctive rhythm of the lines.

5. Link this poem with **"My Tree House" by Charles Ghigna** (1st Grade, Week 12, page 78) or **"My Pet" by David L. Harrison** (2nd Grade, Week 4, page 110), or selections from *Poetrees* by Douglas Florian.

Take 5!

1. **Make a simple sign with the word *Don't* on it** and pass it around the room while you read the poem aloud. Each student can hold it up in turn as you say the word in the poem.

2. **Invite students to join in on the oral reading by saying the word *Don't* together** as you read the rest of the poem aloud.

3. For discussion: *What would life be like without any rules?*

4. Discuss how **poets sometimes use patterns** from things like lists or songs when creating a poem. Here, the poet uses rules and repetition to create a poem for two voices (or two sets of ears).

5. Connect this poem with another poem with parts for two voices, such as **Juanita Havill's "Car Trip"** (3rd Grade, Week 34, page 180) or **"I Might Go to Mars"** (2nd Grade, Week 28, page 134), or selections from *Technically, It's Not My Fault: Concrete Poems* by John Grandits.

THE WAY YOU SOUND
by **John Grandits**

THE WAY YOU SOUND

TO YOU
TO ME

TO YOU	TO ME
No running in the house.	Don't!
Wear a **nice** shirt.	Don't!
Hurry up.	Don't!
The stairs are not a toboggan hill.	Don't!
Do your homework.	Don't!
Pay attention.	Don't!
Turn off the TV.	Don't!
Comb your hair.	Don't!
Are you whining?	Don't!
Pick up your room.	Don't!
Wait until I'm off the phone.	Don't!
Put down that comic book.	Don't!
Be careful when you go outside.	Don't!
Chew your food.	Don't!
Stand up straight.	Don't!
Go outside and play something.	Don't!
Leave your sister alone.	Don't!
Go to your room.	Don't!
Come out from under there.	Don't!
What are you laughing at?	Don't!
Get ready for bed.	Don't!
Skateboards are outside toys.	Don't!
You'll put someone's eye out.	Don't!
Sit still.	Don't do whatever it is you're doing.

SATURDAYS
by **Monica Gunning**

Saturday morning! No school today!
Still no rest for me.
Mean Grandma saddles me with chores.
I gather firewood from the field,
Fetch water from the pond
With a gourd from the calabash fruit.
Shine floors with a coconut brush
On my knees, rough like an alligator's skin.

But on Saturday night
The shops stay open late
In the village square.
The banjo player in high spirits
Strums calypso tunes and sings.
I go to the square, join the singing.
Soon, I'm in a festive mood
Like the lively village crowd.

Take 5!

1. Set the stage for reading this poem aloud by taking a moment to encourage students to close their eyes and imagine an island village in a tropical location. **If necessary, explain words like *calabash*, *gourd*, and *calypso*.**

2. **Share the poem again with student participation,** inviting them to say the first line of each stanza (*Saturday morning! No school today!* and *But on Saturday night*).

3. For discussion: *What kinds of chores do you have to do around the house?*

4. In this lyrical poem, the poet explores emotions and describes experiences. Guide students in talking about which words or lines suggest how the poet feels in this poem (such as *Mean Grandma; high spirits; festive mood*). **What emotions does the poem evoke in us** (in the first stanza, then in the second stanza)?

5. Link this poem with **"The Breakfast Boss" by Janet Wong** (3rd Grade, Week 13, page 159), or look for more autobiographical poems by Monica Gunning in *Under the Breadfruit Tree: Island Poems.*

Take 5!

1. Before reading this poem aloud, **encourage students to listen for clue words in the details** so they can guess the subject of the poem when you have finished reading.

2. Read the poem aloud again, **inviting students to say the last two lines of the poem in unison** (*without ever whispering / a word.*) Cue students by pointing to your ear.

3. For discussion: *If earrings have a "job," what is the job of rings, belts, or socks?*

4. Point out that sometimes poets borrow from other things, like riddles, to create a new poem. **Guide students in identifying the clues and details that suggest the poem's subject** (earrings). Then talk about how the key words (such as *hear, ear, lobe, face*) are arranged (line by line) to dole out the facts bit by bit.

5. Connect this poem with other riddle poems, like **Carol-Ann Hoyte's "It's a Wrap"** (3rd Grade, Week 19, page 165) and "From Root to Tip" (5th Grade, Week 19, page 245), or selections from *Spot the Plot! A Riddle Book of Book Riddles* by J. Patrick Lewis.

RIDDLE
by **Nikki Grimes**

My job is not
to beat the drum,
or help you hear,
however much I cling
or swing from your ear,
or stud your lobe
with globes of glitter.
But, large or small,
I can call attention
to your face,
any time, any place,
without ever whispering
a word.

GIFT UNGIVEN
by **JonArno Lawson**

My favorite gift was a gift ungiven—
You got it for me, but then loved it and kept it.
My favorite gift was a gift ungotten
By me—it's yours—that's fine, I accept it.
I almost feel happy, I almost feel glad
That I almost enjoyed the gift I almost had.

Take 5!

1. If possible, **begin with an empty gift-wrapped box or package** and unwrap it slowly, line by line, as you read the poem aloud.

2. Share the poem again while displaying the words, and **invite students to say lines 1, 3, and 5** (*My favorite gift was a gift ungiven / My favorite gift was a gift ungotten / I almost feel happy, I almost feel glad*) while you read the rest aloud.

3. **Sometimes poets use unusual or archaic words to make their poems even more interesting.** Talk with students about such words in this poem (*ungiven, ungotten*).

4. This poem is another example of humorous poetry. Talk with students about how **the poet creates humor in this poem through wordplay and repetition.** Pinpoint examples in the words and phrases the poet uses.

5. Follow up with another gift poem, **"Appy Birthday" by April Halprin Wayland** (2nd Grade, Week 24, page 130), or selections from JonArno Lawson's poetry book, *Black Stars in a White Night Sky.*

Take 5!

1. Read this poem aloud, noting that it incorporates **a few Spanish words that may need a bit of explaining,** such as *bailes* (dances), *quinceañera* (a coming-out ball for girls on their 15th birthday), *escuincles* (kids), and *cumbias* (plural of a kind of dance), as well as a few words in English that may be unfamiliar (*disgruntled, mesmerize*). If needed, invite a Spanish speaker to assist you with pronunciation.

2. Read the poem aloud again, and **invite students to join in on the final stanza.**

3. **Talk about the Cinderella parts of this poem.**

4. In this lyrical poem, the poet explores emotions and expresses anxieties. Guide students in exploring which lines suggest how the poet feels in this poem. **Stage a "tableau,"** a frozen moment of the poem posed as a "scene," with student volunteers posing as described in each stanza of the poem. How does each tableau reflect the theme(s) of the poem?

5. Connect this poem with another by **Guadalupe Garcia McCall, "Doña Pepita"** (5th Grade, Week 14, page 240).

BAILES
by **Guadalupe Garcia McCall**

Every weekend, without
Fail, I am the fairy godmother
Who helps my sisters dress up
For the ball and escorts
Them to the *bailes* in Mexico.

A *quinceañera* today, a
Wedding tomorrow. We
Always arrive late, and off
They go, gliding on the dance
Floor in their magical
Slippers, while I sit
In a corner, a disgruntled
Toad trapped in a crumpled,
Satin dress and tight pantyhose,
Doomed as the ugly
Stepsisters.
My sisters want to find
Charming husbands. They
Want to get married, be taken
Care of, raise *escuincles* of
Their own. But that's not
What moves me.

I want to raise my arms up
To heaven and touch the sky.
I want to open my petals
And mesmerize the sun.
I don't want to dance
Cumbias in Mexico.
I want to grow wings
And fly around the world.
I want to blossom.

I HAD TO GET A SHOT AT THE DOCTOR'S
by April Halprin Wayland

and my arm hurt
and it still hurts as we get to the dog park
and James and his dogs show up
and we all spill through the double gate
and our red, green and blue leashes tangle
and I am laughing because we are so tangled
and our dogs are so goofy
and now it doesn't hurt.

Take 5!

1. In sharing this poem aloud, **point out to students that the title is actually a line in the poem, too.**

2. **Read the poem aloud again, inviting students to say only the word *and* as it begins every line, with some exaggeration for emphasis.**

3. For discussion: *How do you feel about visiting the doctor or the dentist?*

4. This poem is another example of *free verse*, a poem that does not rhyme. Talk about how the poet turns this list of run-on sentences into a poem by repeating the opening word (*and*), sequencing events in an *If You Give a Mouse a Cookie* order, and using **contrasting opening and closing lines.**

5. Link this poem with **"Dog Walking Tanka" by Margarita Engle** (2nd Grade, Week 31, page 137) or **"Good Dog! Bad Dog!" by Jeannine Atkins** (5th Grade, Week 5, page 231).

Take 5!

1. If you have a Halloween skeleton, display it while reading the poem aloud. Anatomical words may need explaining (*cranium, tibia, humerus*) as well as **made-up words like brainium and fib-ia.**

2. **Invite students to say the phrase "By golly!" with gusto.**

3. **The poet weaves facts into the poem.** Guide students in noting what we learn about the human skeleton in this poem.

4. **Help students identify the rhyming pairs** that occur in each stanza (*shy/guy; brainium/cranium; tibia/fib-ia; numerous/humerus*) including "slant" or "almost" rhymes (*golly/body*) and internal rhymes (*Gangly/O'Dangly; rattle-bone/all alone; shy/guy; hollered/golly*).

5. Follow up with **"Funny Bone (Humerus)" by Michael J. Rosen** (5th Grade, Week 18, page 244).

THE GUY IN THE CLOSET*
by **Heidi Bee Roemer**

Gangly O'Dangly is frightfully shy.
He's a rattle-bone, all alone, kind of a guy.

The first time I saw him, I hollered, "By golly!"
He models the bones that are inside my body.

Alas, there's no brain inside his poor brainium;
Nary a hair grows upon his smooth cranium.

He has two-hundred-six parts, including his tibia.
He hasn't a tongue, so he can't tell a fib-ia.

Gangly is thin. His meals weren't numerous.
Count Gangly's ribs. Can you tickle his humerus?

* model skeleton

I'VE NEVER SEEN A PURPLE COW
by **Lesléa Newman**

I've never seen a purple cow
A hot-pink horse, a light-green sow,
A ruby dog, a turquoise cat
A copper crow, an orange bat,
A green and yellow speckled calf
A black and lavender giraffe,
A sky-blue pig, a dark-red frog
A navy polka-dotted hog,
A violet goat, a cherry hare
An indigo and scarlet bear,
A swarm of bright magenta flies
And if I did, I'd check my eyes.

Take 5!

1. Encourage students to close their eyes and **imagine a hot-pink horse, an orange bat, and a sky-blue pig.** Then continue by reading this poem aloud.

2. Display the poem and **invite students to choose their favorite colorful animal and chime in when that color/ animal phrase appears.**

3. Talk with students about all the **words for different colors** in this poem (purple, hot pink, light green, ruby, turquoise, copper, orange, green and yellow, black and lavender, sky blue, dark red, navy, violet, cherry, indigo, scarlet, magenta).

4. Poets love to play with words and how they are arranged on the page. Here the poem is almost like a list, but with regular end rhymes. **Invite students to tap the rhythm** of the poem as you share it again. Many poems have a beat and meter just like songs do.

5. Share another list poem by **Lesléa Newman, "By the Sea"** (1st Grade, Week 35, page 101), or poems from *Yellow Elephant: A Bright Bestiary* by Julie Larios.

Take 5!

1. Add a bit of fun to sharing this poem with a poetry prop—**show a tree branch** before reading the poem aloud.

2. Share the poem again by inviting students to say only the first word in each line as you read the rest aloud. They can repeat all the "first" words again at the conclusion of the poem. **(The first words make another sentence—the theme of the poem.)**

3. For discussion: *How do we "water" a friendship?*

4. Sometimes poets use each letter of a key word to begin each line of a poem, which is called *acrostic* poetry. Talk about how **this poem is a variation of the acrostic form that uses a key word (rather than a letter only) to begin each line** and how the words add up to a sentence, just as the letters of the usual acrostic poem add up to a word.

5. Look for more acrostic poetry by **Avis Harley** in **"Last Try"** (1st Grade, Week 31, page 97), or read selections from her book *African Acrostics: A Word in Edgeways.*

A BRANCH OF FRIENDSHIP
by **Avis Harley**

Friendship can mean a helping hand: it
Is to say you understand.
A simple scene, but able to
Plant a loyalty where language can't.
We all
Need friends—the want runs deep, for a branch
To hold when the climb is steep. And yet, how
Often we fail to nourish what pines for
Water so its roots may flourish.

POEM FOR A BULLY
by **Eileen Spinelli**

Somewhere deep inside you
there's a softer, kinder place.
I know this will surprise you—
but I've seen it in your face.
Your eyes are often sad, although
you wear a surly grin.
Sometimes when you stand all alone
your "mean" seems worn and thin.
I wish that you would take a step—
a small but brave one, too—
and look inside yourself to find
the good I see in you.

Take 5!

1. Before reading this poem in a soft voice, **point out to students that many poems are funny, but some are serious—like this one.**

2. Share the poem aloud again, and this time **invite students to read the last line together.**

3. For discussion: *How do we help each other be our best selves?*

4. In this lyrical poem, the poet is reaching out to the reader. What details reveal the poet's hopes? **What thoughts or emotions does the poem prompt in us?**

5. Combine this poem with **"The Bully" by Guadalupe Garcia McCall** (5th Grade, Week 22, page 248).

GIVE ME WINGS
by **Graham Denton**

Give me wings
so I may know
the world above
the earth below,
those endless oceans
of the sky
where I can float
and I can fly.

Give me wings
so I may feel
the swoop, the sweep,
the whirl, the wheel,
the beating wind
beneath my breast
as, feathers wide,
I ride the crest.

Give me wings
so I may soar,
a stranger to
all clouds no more,
up where the heavens
have no end;
to moon and sun
and stars, a friend.

Give me wings
so I may be
a bird at last –
unbound and free,
a bird whose heart
forever sings,
unburdened by
this gift of wings.

Take 5!

1. Before sharing the poem aloud, pause to encourage students to close their eyes and **imagine being able to fly, imagine wings, imagine sky.** Then continue by reading this poem aloud.

2. Next, **invite students to join together on the first line of each stanza**, *Give me wings* (also the title of the poem).

3. For discussion: ***Where would you go if you had wings to fly?***

4. In this lyrical poem, **the poet uses *alliteration* to repeat the same sound(s) in the beginning of several words** for greater emphasis. Help students locate examples of this (e.g., *swoop/sweep; whirl/wheel; beneath/breast*).

5. Link this poem with **"Explorer" by Joan Bransfield Graham** (3rd Grade, Week 23, page 169), or selections from *Give Me Wings*, edited by Lee Bennett Hopkins.

SUPER KEY MAN
by Esther Hershenhorn

My keyboard has me thinking,
What a Super Hero I'd be,
If I were a computer,
Instead of human me.

I'd say and do what all I pleased,
The keys my Hero's cape.
And should my words and deeds
bring Trouble,
I'd quickly click ESCAPE.

And if that failed to do the trick,
If Trouble chose to roam,
I'd finger my way 'cross the rows
'til I pressed down on HOME.

And *still* if Trouble cornered me,
Proving extra fleet.
I'd let him think he'd finally won,
then *Presto!* jab DELETE.

And if, by chance, *I* disappear,
I'd stand tall, resolute.
I'd turn me off, then on again.
Super Key Man can always REBOOT!

Take 5!

1. If possible, **read this poem from a computer** or while your computer is on. Click on each key as it is mentioned at the end of each stanza of the poem (*escape, home, delete*), and then reboot at the end.

2. In follow-up readings, **invite kids to say the "key" words at the end of each stanza** (*escape, home, delete, reboot*) while you read the rest of the poem aloud.

3. For discussion: *If you could have a super-power, what would it be?*

4. Poets give their poems shape and structure in many different ways. Talk with students about each stanza in this poem and what it adds to the poem. **Consider the poet's use of italics and capital letters, too.**

5. Contrast this poem with another about real-life heroes, **"Fire!" by Laura Purdie Salas** (1st Grade, Week 14, page 80), or look for more playful hero poems in *The Superheroes Employment Agency* by Marilyn Singer.

Take 5!

1. Read this poem aloud with a bit of pantomiming. Hop around rhythmically while reading the first part of the poem, then **hop crazily as if you just got an ant bite** on your ankle while reading the second part of the poem.

2. Share the poem again, **inviting students to join in on the hopping.** They can say the word *No* loudly as the poem (and the hopping) takes a turn.

3. **Encourage students to share their own picnic stories.**

4. Sometimes poets use basic graphic elements and spatial arrangement to shape their poems. **Lead students in discussing how this poet places the words on the page,** and even separates letters in words or aligns words on the right side instead of the left side. Talk about how this guides our reading, and then read the poem aloud together again.

5. Connect this poem with **"Beats on Top of Your Head"** (5th Grade, Week 25, page 251) **by Jaime Adoff,** son of Arnold Adoff.

YOU THINK THIS IS A DANCE
by **Arnold Adoff**

```
You   Think   This   Is   A   Dance

Some      Hip
          Hop
          Hap
           p
           y    Kind  Of  A  Stomp
                          Around A
                          Plate Of
                            Fancy
                          Cookies
          On   A Picnic   Afternoon

          No      This  Is  A  Giant
                           A n t
                 Sharpening
                 HisPincers    On
                               My
                 Ankle Bone
                 I nS i d e
                 My  Floppy
                 S   o   c   k
```

WHY HIPPOS LOOK BAKED
by **J. Patrick Lewis**

If you own a pet hippo,
That big baked potato
Has the look and feel
Of sunburned Play-Doh.

The first thing to do
Is remove all the mud,
But don't stick a fork
In that overgrown spud.

If you own a potato
The size of a bus,
That makes it a hippo-
Potato-mus.

Take 5!

1. If possible, **bring a potato as a prop** to set the stage. Then read this poem aloud slowly, enunciating each word.

2. Read the poem aloud again, **inviting students to join in on the words *hippo, potato, spud*, and *hippo-potato-mus*, the key comparison words in the poem.**

3. For discussion: ***What is your favorite vegetable?***

4. Poets compare one thing to another to give us a fresh perspective on both things. **Lead the students in talking about how the potato and the hippo are alike. Use details from the poem.**

5. Another poem that give personality to vegetables is **"My Carrots Are Angry" by Jack Prelutsky** (2nd Grade, Week 33, page 139), or share selections from *If You Were a Chocolate Mustache* by J. Patrick Lewis.

THE ELDERS TOLD ME
by **Joseph Bruchac**

Take 5!

1. Before reading this poem aloud, point out to students that **many poems are funny, but some are quiet and thoughtful—like this one based on beliefs of the Abenaki people.**

2. Share the poem aloud again, **inviting students to join in on key lines**—line 1 (*Speech is mist*), line 5 (*as sacred breath*), and line 10 (*just as the wind*)—while you read the rest aloud.

3. **Talk with students about the world's many languages and which are familiar to them.**

4. Discuss with students how many poems rhyme, but not all. **This poem is an example of *free verse*. It doesn't rhyme, but guide students in seeing how the lines and line breaks build to create a poem in a connected way** (*mist, water, breath, tongue, wind, song,* etc.)

5. Link this poem with **"Poem Like the Sea" by Patricia Hubbell** (3rd Grade, Week 29, page 175).

Speech is mist
lifting from
the small waters
of the mouth
as sacred breath
passes over
the rainbow
of the tongue
that holds every color
just as the wind
contains the notes
of the song
that is all life

ARCHEOLOGY OF A BOOK
by **Betsy Franco**

Remove
my words.
Remove
my art.
My story
unravels
back
to the start.

Remove
my pages,
spine,
design.
What's left?
An idea
in the author's
mind.

Take 5!

1. After reading this poem aloud, you may need to **discuss the word *archeology***.

2. In a follow-up reading, **invite the students to say the word *Remove* each time it occurs in the poem.**

3. The poet weaves factual details into the poem. **Talk with students about the elements of a book** that are noted here.

4. Poets give their poems shape and structure in many ways. **Talk with students about how the short lines and line breaks give this very vertical poem a distinctive rhythm.** Consider the poet's use of rhyme, too (*art/start; spine/design/mind*), including end rhyme, internal rhyme, and slant rhyme.

5. Share another book-related poem, **"The Book" by Stephanie Calmenson** (Kindergarten, Week 28, page 54), or selections from *BookSpeak!: Poems about Books* by Laura Purdie Salas.

Take 5!

1. **Encourage students to close their eyes and think about their surroundings**, both inside and outside. Pause and then read this poem aloud in a quiet voice.

2. Read the poem again, **inviting students to join in on the word *Today*,** which begins several lines of the poem, while you read the rest aloud.

3. **Ask students to pay attention to details on their way from school to home TODAY**—particularly sights and sounds.

4. **This is a lyrical *first person* poem** that reveals what the poet notices in a single day. Talk with students about what the poet sees (in lines 2, 3, 4) and hears (in lines 8, 9, 10), gleaning details from the poem.

5. Share **"Recipe for a Poem" by Kristy Dempsey** (2nd Grade, Week 29, page 135).

TODAY
by **Eileen Spinelli**

Today I'm going to pay attention.
To the broken blueness of sky.
To the high weeds in the vacant lot.
To the rusted pot in the alleyway.
Today I'm going to leap across puddles
and steep in green
and all the wild colors in between.
I'm going to listen to
what the birds are singing about,
and to the happy shouts of toddlers on swings.
Today I'm going to gather all my heart can hold
of lemony light and yawning cats
and the bright blur of traffic on the bridge.
Today I'm going to pay attention.
Today I'm going to find myself a poem.

THE KANGAROOSTER
by Jack Prelutsky

The KANGAROOSTER does not yawn
When it arises, right at dawn.
Instead, as if to spread the news,
It loudly cock-a-doodle-doos.
When it's wakened everyone
In time to see the morning sun,
It puffs its chest and pecks the air,
Then struts about with pride and flair.

When these proceedings are complete,
It springs away on giant feet.
With every monumental bound,
It covers yards and yards of ground.
As it continues down the trail,
It flourishes its massive tail.
Then, with one final mighty leap,
It yawns at last, and falls asleep.

Take 5!

1. **While reading this poem aloud, sketch a picture of the creature** (as in Pictionary) based on the details that are shared in the poem bit by bit. The sillier, the better!

2. Display the poem and read it aloud again, pausing before the final rhyming word in each rhyming pair. **Invite students to complete the rhyme by saying the word out loud.**

3. For discussion: *What other unusual combinations can you think of using animals with multisyllable names?* (For example: tiger + giraffe = tiraffe; monkey + crocodile = monkodile.)

4. **This poem is an example of a narrative poem—a poem that tells a story.** Guide students in seeing how the lines and stanzas build to create a poem framed by two lines about yawning.

5. Then follow up with a poem about yawns, **"Catching a Yawn" by Avis Harley** (3rd Grade, Week 18, page 164), or selections from Jack Prelutsky's book, *Behold the Bold Umbrellaphant: And Other Poems.*

CORN, BEFORE THE BUTTER
by **Laura Purdie Salas**

fields
furrowed, seeded
growing, greening, stretching
sunshine, crows, rainfall, rows
silking, drying, harvesting
sweet, juicy
cobs

Take 5!

1. Add a bit of fun to sharing this poem with a poetry prop—**show an ear of corn, a corn cob, or even a can of corn** before reading the poem aloud.

2. **Invite the students to join you in reading the poem aloud again by saying the first line (*fields*) and the last line (*cobs*) while you read the rest.**

3. For discussion: *What foods do we get from farms (and which can we grow ourselves)?*

4. Many poems rhyme, but not all. **This is an example of a poem form that usually does not rhyme, a diamante poem (a seven-line, diamond-shaped poem based on two contrasting ideas).** Guide students in understanding the form with this example.

5. Connect this poem with **"Pumpkin" by Jane Yolen** (3rd Grade, Week 11, page 157), or selections from *Lettuce Introduce You: Poems about Food* by Laura Purdie Salas.

CROCODILE
by Deborah Chandra

Upon
the watery
deeps
he lives,
and floats
the timbers
of his ribs.

The cargo
of his belly
rides
heavy
in his iron hide.

Mouth
half sunk,
jaws snapped tight,
  drifting
      like a barge at night
  with all lights off,
an empty deck,
as if there's no one there,
      except . . .
above
the darkness
of his brain—
two eye-bumps like
bright window panes.

Take 5!

1. Before you read this poem aloud, **play a short video of a crocodile lurking in the water** for added impact. Or use it without sound while reading the poem. One source is Video.NationalGeographic.com.

2. Share the poem again with student participation, **inviting them to say the line** *except . . .* and pause dramatically before reading the rest of the poem.

3. For discussion: *What boat-related words does the poet use to describe the crocodile?* (For example, *timbers, cargo, iron, barge, deck.*)

4. Poets give their poems shape and structure in many ways. **Talk with students about how the short lines, line breaks, and stanzas give this poem a distinctive rhythm.** Consider the poet's use of spacing, particularly the indenting of words in the third stanza. Then read the whole poem aloud together again.

5. Link this poem with **"Crocodile" by Ann Whitford Paul** (1st Grade, Week 7, page 73).

Take 5!

1. As you read this poem aloud, **add your own sound effects to fit the poem's meaning** at the end of various lines (e.g., for *lightning, thunder, dog, rain, door, boy*).

2. This time, display the text of the poem and **invite students to read the second half of every line,** pausing at the comma for them to complete each line.

3. **Review emergency preparations for imminent storms.**

4. Sometimes poets use their imaginations to guess what it might be like if something that is not alive had a real personality. This technique is called *personification.* Guide the students in determining **which words or lines in this poem suggest that *clouds, lightning, thunder, rain,* and *door* have human feelings.**

5. Follow up this poem by revisiting **"Bird Alert: Storm Warning!" by Constance Levy** (4th Grade, Week 8, page 194), or selections from *Sharing the Seasons,* edited by Lee Bennett Hopkins.

SUMMER STORM
by Irene Latham

Cloud warns, *get ready.*
Lightning spits, *all clear.*
Thunder growls, *Hello, Dog.*
Dog yips, *get out of here!*

Rain roars, *is that all you've got?*
Dog whimpers, *go away.*
Door whispers, *come inside.*
Boy breathes, *it'll be okay.*

CROSSING THE INTERNATIONAL DATE LINE
by **Joan Bransfield Graham**

On Tuesday at 4 PM,
   our trip ended—
      we departed.
We got back home
Tuesday 7 AM,
   to arrive
before we started!

Note: This happened when
we went to New Zealand.

Take 5!

1. **Highlight the time on a nearby clock** before reading this poem aloud.

2. Share the poem again, but this time **invite students to say lines 1 and 5** (*On Tuesday at 4 PM; Tuesday 7 AM*) while you read the rest aloud.

3. **Challenge students to "do the math," calculating how long the trip in the poem actually took.**

4. **Talk with students about the arrangement of words and line breaks** in this poem and where the crucial rhyming words occur (*departed/started*). Then read the poem aloud again, emphasizing the rhyming words in particular.

5. Follow up with another poem about travel, **"Directions" by Janet Wong** (5th Grade, Week 34, page 260).

Take 5!

1. For a poetry prop, **place a backpack in front of you** and then read the poem aloud.

2. Read the poem aloud again. **Invite students to SHOUT the lines** *"where is the / vacuum cleaner?"* when you get to them as you read the rest of the poem.

3. For discussion: ***When you pack for a trip, what do you hate to leave behind?***

4. This is another example of an *acrostic* poem in which the poet uses the first letter of a key word to begin each line of a poem. **Talk about how this poem is a variation of the acrostic form that uses two key words** (*family vacation*) rather than only one, and how those words are also the title of the poem.

5. Share another packing poem, **"No Way!" by David L. Harrison** (Kindergarten, Week 35, page 61), or selections from *Vacation, We're Going to the Ocean!*, also by David L. Harrison.

FAMILY VACATION
by **Kathi Appelt**

First, we pack
all our underwear, five
matched pairs of socks, toothbrush, deodorant,
in a knapsack that won't zip,
lug it to the car where
your dad shouts, "where is the

vacuum cleaner?"
as if it were normal to
cart such a thing, right
along with the family dog,
Topper, who gets
indigestion, even with the window
open, even
now.

CENTIPEDE
by **Michael J. Rosen**

Beneath the lawn, on the slimy bottoms
of logs and stones,
among the fallen, rotten, and sodden,
where every root
hoards the sun's renewing beams,
the centipedes
create the planet's future, turning
what once had been
into what might yet be: an aspen,
a milkweed pod,
a field of beans or pumpkins.

Take 5!

1. Create a visual backdrop for this poem by **sharing a video (without sound) showing a centipede in action** (see Video.NationalGeographic.com). Then read the poem aloud slowly as students watch and listen.

2. Share the poem aloud again, and **invite students to say line 6 (*the centipedes*) together** while you read the rest of the poem.

3. For discussion: *How does the past help shape our future?*

4. This poet weaves several factual details into the poem. Guide students in noting what we learn about centipedes in this poem. **For a contrasting approach, research information from nonfiction sources**. Then read the poem aloud together again.

5. Share a silly centipede poem, **"A Centipede's Excuse" by Kristy Dempsey** (1st Grade, Week 34, page 100), or look for *Nasty Bugs,* edited by Lee Bennett Hopkins.

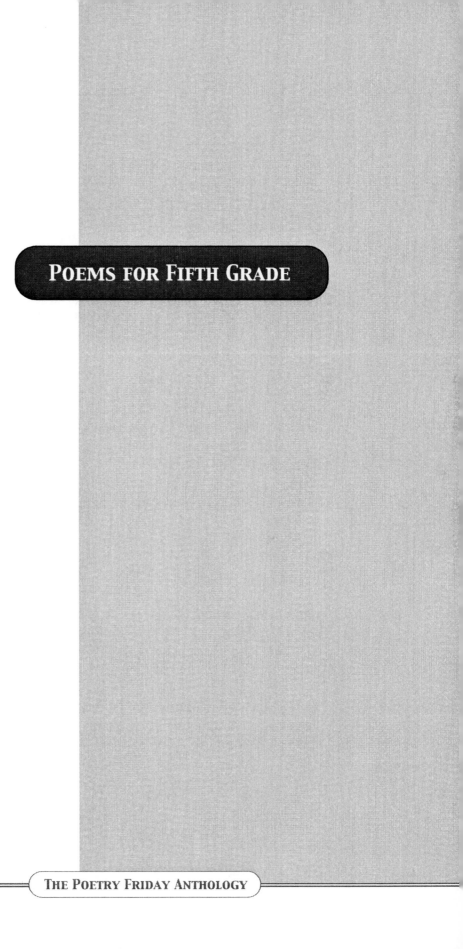

POEMS FOR FIFTH GRADE

Common Core Standards for Fifth Grade
(RL.5.2; RL.5.4; RL.5.5; RL.5.6; RL.5.7)

In sharing poetry with fifth graders, we support their expanding vocabularies, promote a playful awareness of words and language, and develop their confidence in comprehending texts of all kinds.

First we focus on enjoyment and understanding, and then we guide students in responding to poetry in various forms, and in articulating themes from key ideas and details in the poems and from how the poem's speaker reflects upon and shapes a topic with a particular point of view.

In sharing poetry aloud and in print, we can guide students in understanding word meanings and how figurative language like metaphors and similes function in poetry.

We can help them understand how structural elements like stanzas and line breaks help shape a poem and how visual and multimedia elements contribute to the meaning, tone, or beauty of a poem.

In fun and participatory ways, we can celebrate poetry while gently introducing and reinforcing key skills.

week 1	School	The World's Most Intelligent Chicken *by Jack Prelutsky*
week 2	More School	Backpack *by Irene Latham*
week 3	Fun & Games	Equipment Haiku *by Jen Bryant*
week 4	Pets	What's the Opposite . . . *by Ann Whitford Paul*
week 5	More Pets	Good Dog! Bad Dog! *by Jeannine Atkins*
week 6	On the Ground	Earthworms *by Michael J. Rosen*
week 7	In the Water	Green Sea Turtle *by Steven Withrow*
week 8	In the Air	How the Geese Became Chiefs of the Birds *by Joseph Bruchac*
week 9	Weather	Apprehended by Autumn *by Kristy Dempsey*
week 10	Food	Tomato Sandwiches *by Kathi Appelt*
week 11	More Food	Flapjack Flip *by Heidi Bee Roemer*
week 12	House & Home	A Real Bed *by Monica Gunning*
week 13	Families	Waiting *by Nikki Grimes*
week 14	Community	Doña Pepita *by Guadalupe Garcia McCall*
week 15	Stuff We Love	Charm Bracelet *by Charles Waters*
week 16	Holidays	Get a Life *by Eileen Spinelli*
week 17	Time Together	Greetings *by Lesléa Newman*
week 18	Human Body	Funny Bone (Humerus) *by Michael J. Rosen*
week 19	More Human Body	From Root to Tip *by Carol-Ann Hoyte*
week 20	Art & Colors	Paint Mind *by Susan Marie Swanson*
week 21	Love & Friendship	You Misbehave *by Gail Carson Levine*
week 22	A Kinder Place	The Bully *by Guadalupe Garcia McCall*
week 23	Exploring	Cold War *by Margarita Engle*
week 24	Science & Tech	Wheel of Progress *by Juanita Havill*
week 25	Song & Dance	Beats on Top of Your Head *by Jaime Adoff*
week 26	Nonsense	How to Open the Attic Door *by April Halprin Wayland*
week 27	World of Words	First Take *by Jane Yolen*
week 28	Books	My Sister Lisette *by Carmen T. Bernier-Grand*
week 29	Poetry Poems	How Is a Meadow an Ocean? *by Laura Purdie Salas*
week 30	RR&R	Cerberus *by Linda Ashman*
week 31	Different Forms	House Mouse *by Laura Purdie Salas*
week 32	Metaphor & Simile	Night Comes *by Deborah Chandra*
week 33	Personification	"Things are looking up" *by Heidi Mordhorst*
week 34	On the Move	Directions *by Janet Wong*
week 35	Summer Vacation	Family Vacation *by Allan Wolf*
week 36	Looking Forward	When the Future Arrives *by Bobbi Katz*

*"At funerals, graduations, fiftieth wedding anniversaries, birthday parties, at the inauguration of a president, **people gather to read**—what? Not stories. Not articles or plays. They read **poems**."*

❧ Ralph Fletcher ❧

Take 5!

1. Show a test answer sheet and **bubble in responses as you read the poem aloud.** You can find printable answer sheets at TeacherVision.Fen.com.

2. **Next, invite students to participate in reading the poem aloud with you.** Display the words of the poem so students can read aloud the nonsensical lines of the middle stanza while you read the rest.

3. For discussion: *Which would you rather be, chicken or duck?*

4. Sometimes poets like to use **many words that start the same (alliteration)** to add to the sound of the poem. Challenge students to identify the words beginning with repeated sounds in this poem (*world's, wisest; knew nearly nothing; math, music; supposed, smart*). Note that in the case of *n*, there are two different letter combinations that spell that sound: *kn* and *n*. Read the poem aloud together again, emphasizing these words in particular.

5. Follow up this poem with **"Feeling Jumpy" by Patricia Hubbell** (4th Grade, Week 1, page 187), or selections from *Countdown to Summer* by J. Patrick Lewis.

THE WORLD'S MOST INTELLIGENT CHICKEN
by **Jack Prelutsky**

The world's most intelligent chicken,
As well as the world's wisest duck,
Were challenged to take an IQ test—
They agreed with a quack and a cluck.
For fowl that were rated so highly,
Their knowledge turned out to be small.
In fact, it was quickly apparent
They knew nearly nothing at all.

They thought that an ibis had petals,
They thought that an iris had wings.
They thought that potatoes grew feathers,
They thought that a cantaloupe sings.
They thought that a floor needed windows,
That apples grew under the sea,
That clocks always ran counterclockwise,
And eight minus seven was three.

They struggled with every last question
On science, math, music, and art.
You'd never suspect, from their answers,
That they were supposed to be smart.
They filled in the blanks incorrectly,
Their two little brains remained stuck . . .
A chicken is only a chicken,
A duck is no more than a duck.

BACKPACK
by **Irene Latham**

I'd say paper
is my favorite feast—
I love it spiraled,
bound or loose-leaf.

(Pencils poke,
 rulers break.
Textbooks give me
 a belly ache.)

Whatever you feed me,
I'll do my best;
you're the one
who takes the tests!

Take 5!

1. For a poetry prop, **place a backpack in front of you and then read the poem aloud.**

2. For a follow-up reading, **invite students to echo read the last stanza of the poem,** repeating each line of the last stanza after you read it aloud. Then read the rest of the poem aloud again by yourself.

3. For discussion: *Do different backpacks have different personalities?*

4. **Sometimes poets use their imaginations to guess what it might be like if something that is not alive had a real personality. This technique is called *personification*.** Guide the students in determining which words or lines in this poem suggest that the backpack has human feelings (*feast, belly ache, feed*). Note that the first person voice in the poem is also a clue.

5. Connect this poem with **"Ready" by Joan Bransfield Graham** (1st Grade, Week 1, page 67), or selections from *School Supplies*, edited by Lee Bennett Hopkins.

Take 5!

1. **Show a piece of sports equipment** (a shin guard, mouth guard, soccer ball, or cleats) **before reading the poem aloud.**

2. **Share the poem aloud again, this time displaying the words. Invite students to join in** the first line in the first two poems (*"Good heavens, they stink!"; Tastes like burned rubber*) and the last line in the last two poems (*when I whiff a kick; spike prints in moon sand*).

3. For discussion: *What is your favorite piece of sports equipment?*

4. This is an example of a poem form that usually does not rhyme (but sometimes does), a haiku poem. **Originally a Japanese form of poetry, a haiku is made up of three lines (generally 5 syllables, 7 syllables, 5 syllables) and often refers to nature or the outdoors.** Guide students in understanding the haiku form with these four examples.

5. Link these poems with another sports-themed haiku, **"Fifty Yard Dash" by Lorie Ann Grover** (4th Grade, Week 2, page 188), or selections from *And the Crowd Goes Wild!: A Global Gathering of Sports Poems*, edited by Carol-Ann Hoyte and Heidi Bee Roemer.

EQUIPMENT HAIKU
by **Jen Bryant**

SHIN GUARDS

"Good heavens, they stink!"
That's what my Mom says when I
set them in her sink.

MOUTH GUARD

Tastes like burned rubber.
Hard, plastic, electric blue;
annoying smile shield.

BALL

That black and white sphere,
my would-be best friend, except
when I whiff a kick.

CLEATS

Astronauts could wear
special space-made pairs, leaving
spike prints in moon sand.

WHAT'S THE OPPOSITE . . .
by **Ann Whitford Paul**

What's the opposite of racing everywhere?
Dozing, composed on an easy chair.
What's the opposite of leaping for a treat?
Inspecting before one deigns to eat.
What's the opposite of a noisy yip-yap bark?
A whispery soft, purred remark.
All of this then settles that
the opposite of dog is cat!

Take 5!

1. Read this poem aloud using **a louder, faster voice for lines 1, 3, 5, and 7, and a softer, slower voice for lines 2, 4, 6, and 8.** You might need to explain some words, such as *deign.*

2. Next, display the words of the poem and **invite the cat lovers to read lines 2, 4, 6, and 8** (in "cat" voices) **and the dog lovers to read lines 1, 3, 5, and 7** (in "dog" voices).

3. **Survey students about their preferences for dogs vs. cats.**

4. Sometimes poets use words that mimic sounds, which is called *onomatopoeia.* Challenge the students to find examples in this poem (*yip-yap*) and talk about how that affects the meaning of the poem. **We sometimes use one word to describe making a sound (such as *purr*) and another word to describe the sound itself (*meow*).** Use this poem to explore this concept further (*purr; yip-yap*).

5. Connect this poem with **"Rough and Tumble" by Lesléa Newman** (2nd Grade, Week 30, page 136), or selections from *A Curious Collection of Cats* by Betsy Franco.

Take 5!

1. To kick off this poem, show images of the two masks of drama—comedy and tragedy. Then **read this poem aloud using a light and happy voice for lines 1, 3, 5, 7, 9, 11, 12** and a frustrated voice for lines 2, 4, 6, 8, 10.

2. Next, display the words of the poem and **divide the students into two groups—one to say the words** *Good dog* **as they occur in the poem and one to say the words** *Bad dog.* You read the rest of the poem, including the conclusion of lines beginning *Good dog* or *Bad dog.*

3. **Invite students to share their own favorite pet stories.**

4. Poets give their poems shape and meaning in many ways. Talk with students about each stanza and what it adds to the poem. **Consider the poet's use of rhyme (***bed/bread; chair/care***) and how the rhyme depends on the final syllable in one case (***heart/apart).

5. Follow up with more dog poems, like **"Spotty's Tongue" by Betsy Franco** (3rd Grade, Week 5, page 151) or **"My Dog Jack Thinks Up His Valentine" by Patricia Hubbell** (2nd Grade, Week 21, page 127), or selections from Betsy Franco's book, *A Dazzling Display of Dogs.*

GOOD DOG! BAD DOG!
by **Jeannine Atkins**

Good dog never wakes us up.
Yip! Bad dog jumps on the bed.
Good dog shakes for a biscuit.
Bad dog snitches jam and bread.

Good dog chews dog toys.
Bad dog chews the chair.
Good dog comes when called.
Bad dog doesn't care.

Good dog snuggles by my feet.
Bad dog steals my heart.
No, that's our good dog!
Some days we can't tell them apart.

EARTHWORMS
by **Michael J. Rosen**

Soil—that's our crop. Without our lot,
nothing of yours will grow. We burrow, swallow—
dust, motes of dirt, mold, rootlets—
and cast the sweet earth within your plot.

If you could see the tunnels, the catacombs
our millions have wound beneath your feet!
But nothing we do lasts. We make our way
toward home by making every way a home.

Honestly, people, we're the planet's earthlings.
You're just a bunch of heavy human beings.

Take 5!

1. As a poetry prop, bring a jar, baggie, or small pile of dirt. Then **read the poem aloud slowly, sifting the dirt as you read.**

2. To follow up, display the words and **invite students to join in on reading the last two lines** of the poem aloud with you.

3. Sometimes poets weave facts into their poems. **Guide students in noting what information we learn** about earthworms in this poem.

4. Poems usually rhyme at the end of lines, but sometimes they rhyme in the middle too, which is called *internal rhyme*. **Challenge students to find pairs of words that demonstrate internal rhyme** (*grow/burrow/swallow*), including "slant" or "almost" rhymes (*crop/lot; motes/mold*). Then read the poem aloud again.

5. Check out another descriptive poem by **Michael J. Rosen, "Centipede"** (4th Grade, Week 36, page 222).

Take 5!

1. Before reading this poem, **play a video clip of green sea turtles (without sound)** to set the stage, or to use as a background while you read the poem aloud. One source is ConserveTurtles.org/media.php?page=video.

2. Read the poem aloud again, displaying the text of the poem and **inviting students to read the first line of each stanza.**

3. For discussion: *How can we help conserve endangered animals like the green sea turtle?*

4. **Talk about how the facts are presented and why a key detail (*one hundred years...*) might be repeated.**

5. Share another fact-filled poem, **"The Star-Nosed Mole" by Leslie Bulion** (2nd Grade, Week 7, page 113).

GREEN SEA TURTLE
by **Steven Withrow**

One hundred years she learned to swim,
To slow her breath, and to exhale,
Not breaching like a pilot whale
On surfacing at ocean's rim,
But peeking out her bony beak
To taste a gulp of gusty air.

One hundred years to reach full size,
To earn each scar that scores her back,
Engravings from a shark attack,
To win the wisdom of her eyes.
What tales she'd tell if she could speak!
But I can only stand and stare.

HOW THE GEESE BECAME CHIEFS OF THE BIRDS
by **Joseph Bruchac**

Long ago it is said
when the small birds flew
south for the winter
and north for the spring,
sometimes they got lost
and could not find their way.

So Gluskonba
spoke to the geese.
From now on,
you will be the chiefs
of all the birds.

Some of you will go first,
make arrows in the sky
to point the other birds
where to fly.

And some of you
will be the last
to fly north or south
so you can make sure
those small birds
do not lose their way.

And so it is to this day.

Take 5!

1. Point out to students that many poems are funny, but some are quiet and thoughtful —like this one based on a Native American legend from the Abenaki people. You may also need to **provide background on *Gluskonba*, known as "the one who helps the people."**

2. Next, **divide the students into two groups**—one to read the third stanza and one to read the fourth stanza while you read the rest of the poem, including the final line. Display the text of the poem to provide support.

3. For discussion: *Which do you prefer: leading or helping in a supporting role?*

4. Talk with students about how many poems rhyme, but not all. **This poem is an example of *free verse*.** It doesn't feature a regular rhyme, but guide students in seeing the rhythm provided by the structure of short lines and key words used to paint a picture in your mind.

5. Pair this poem with **"How the Birds Got Their Colors" by Joseph Bruchac** (3rd Grade, Week 20, page 166).

Take 5!

1. **Read this poem aloud while pantomiming a few of the motions** suggested in the poem (wind blowing or whistling, raising one hand, raising another hand, dropping hands).

2. **Share the poem again with student participation.** Display the poem and invite students to read lines 5 and 6 together (*first one hand, / then another*) while raising each hand, and then dropping their hands when you read line 7.

3. For discussion: *What are your favorite things about fall?*

4. Guide the students in identifying examples of *personification*, the **key words or lines in this poem that humanize the maple tree**, the subject of the poem (such as *red-handed, desperado, hand*). Share the poem aloud together again.

5. Connect this poem with another about a maple tree, **"The Front Yard Where the Maple Tree Stands" by Allan Wolf** (4th Grade, Week 12, page 198), or selections from *Red Sings from Treetops: A Year in Colors* by Joyce Sidman.

APPREHENDED BY AUTUMN
by **Kristy Dempsey**

A strong arm of wind
whistles at a crooked maple.
Caught red-handed,
the shady desperado raises
first one hand,
then another,
dropping its golden stash
in surrender.

TOMATO SANDWICHES
by **Kathi Appelt**

Sister June's sandwiches held us
all the way to Houston from
the bus stop outside of Blessing.
A sliced tomato from her backyard garden,
laid lovingly atop two pieces of thick
white bread, crusts trimmed,
a thin coating of French's mustard
bought the day before
from Lazlo's Corner Store.
"Ain't no therefore about it," she claims.
And she places the sandwiches in a
brown paper bag along with a jar of
fresh figs. We suck on them
one at a time as the bus rolls
down the narrow road.
When you pray as mightily
as Sister June, tomato sandwiches
will hold you, will help you find
the way to go. "So much comes
from sand," she says. "So much
comes from sand."

Take 5!

1. Bring a wrapped-up sandwich or **a simple brown paper lunch bag as a poetry prop** to show before reading this poem aloud.

2. **Invite students to participate in the oral reading** by reading the words attributed to Sister June in quotation marks in line 10 (*"Ain't no therefore about it"*) and lines 19-21 (*"So much comes / from sand..." / "So much / comes from sand"*).

3. For discussion: *Do you have favorite memories of family gatherings?*

4. **This poem is another example of** *free verse.* Guide students in seeing how the lines and line breaks build to create a poem, one line at a time. Talk with them about how the poet uses the quotes from Sister June to reinforce themes in the poem.

5. Link this poem with another philosophical poem involving something "coming from sand," **"A Clam" by Jack Prelutsky** (3rd Grade, Week 7, page 153).

Take 5!

1. **Bring a spatula to gesture with while reading this pancake poem** aloud. Use it to pantomime words in the poem like *Flip, Slide,* and *Rotate.*

2. Then **invite the students to say the words in bold** (*Flip, Slide,* and *Rotate)* with enthusiasm while you read the rest of the poem aloud. Cue them with the spatula.

3. Here, the poet presents descriptive directions in a sequence resembling a recipe. **Talk with students about the steps they might use for making flapjacks or pancakes.** You can also connect *flip* and *rotate* to a quick introduction to geometry or computer graphics.

4. Help students find the rhyming pairs of words that occur at the end of alternating lines (*great/plate; treat/eat*) including **"slant" or "almost" rhymes (*griddle/sizzle; cream/seen*).** Display the poem and read it aloud again, emphasizing these words in particular.

5. Pair this poem with **"Who Invented Cookies?" by Joan Bransfield Graham** (Kindergarten, Week 10, page 36).

FLAPJACK FLIP
by **Heidi Bee Roemer**

Golden circles.
Hot griddle.
Pancakes bake.
Bubbly sizzle.

Flip the flapjacks.
Lookin' great!
Slide pancakes
on my plate.

Decorate with
whipping cream.
Rotate cakes
so face is seen.

Butter? Syrup?
What a treat.
Yay for pancakes!
Let's eat.

A REAL BED
by **Monica Gunning**

Wouldn't it be grand to sleep
On a real bed with springs
And a mattress like my best friend has?
All I've ever had
Was the banana leaf mattress
I made myself.

Grandpa cuts off
Some dried banana leaves.
I tear and stuff them
Into a flour sack
Till the sack gets full
And that's my bed.

The first few nights are fun
Like jumping onto a pile
Of autumn leaves.
They make a crackling sound.
I twist and turn to hear
Leaves crackle till I fall asleep.

Too soon the leaves crumple
And the crackling's gone.
The mattress gets so flat
It's like sleeping on the bare floor.
Wouldn't it be grand to sleep
On a real bed with springs?

Take 5!

1. Before reading this poem in a soft voice, point out to students that **many poems are funny, but some are serious—like this one.** You may need to explain what a banana leaf or flour sack is, or show images to provide background.

2. **Display the words of the poem and invite students to join in by reading the second stanza aloud** while you read the rest of the poem.

3. **Talk with students about local organizations that help children** and families find beds, shelter, and homes.

4. In this lyrical poem, the poet explores emotions and personal experiences. Guide students in talking about the details that emerge in each stanza and the feelings the poet expresses. **What emotions does the poem evoke in us?**

5. Share another poem about a helpful grandfather, **"Grandfather's Chopsticks" by Janet Wong** (1st Grade, Week 11, page 77).

Take 5!

1. What do baseball legend Babe Ruth, Wendy's restaurant founder Dave Thomas, activist Malcolm X, Apple genius Steve Jobs, and actress Marilyn Monroe all have in common? They were all adopted or grew up in orphanages. **Share the following sensitive poem on this topic, slowly and quietly.**

2. Read the poem again and **invite students to raise their hands and say the lines in quotation marks** (*"Pick me! Pick me!"*) as you read the rest aloud.

3. **Talk with students about local community projects that help children in need.**

4. Poets compare one thing to another to give us a fresh perspective on both things, often using similes and metaphors. **Lead the students in talking about how the child in the poem feels like a "run-down clock" (simile) and "half-past loving" (metaphor).** Use these and other examples from the poem to guide discussion.

5. Share a happier poem about a family photograph, **"Photo Op" by Linda Sue Park** (1st Grade, Week 16, page 82), or selections from *Meet Danitra Brown* by Nikki Grimes.

WAITING
by **Nikki Grimes**

The orphanage
put my picture
on a postcard.
My smile says
"Pick me! Pick me!"
But mostly, people say
I'm too old to adopt,
like I'm a run-down clock
and the big hand says
Julie is half-past loving.

DOÑA PEPITA
by **Guadalupe Garcia McCall**

Doña Pepita has three sons
Who run away when she needs
Help in the garden.
My brother calls her Chubby Chencha.
Her dark eyes twinkle like falling stars
When she grins at him, because
She doesn't understand English.
"*¡Que Chula!*" she says
When I come over to help pull weeds
And water the lawn. I follow along
As she limps through the jungle
Of her backyard. A groggy spider
Watches us from her spindly throne
And an orchestra of lazy crickets
Plays a distorted tune.
Doña Pepita bends over
And with her knife she cuts
The vines that free the *calabazita*,
A freckled zucchini she has been
Nurturing there all season.
It is now the size of a newborn baby.
Doña Pepita cradles it in her arms
And coos as she dusts it off.
"*¿Que bonita, verdad?*" she says,
Waiting for my approval.
I nod my head and she hands it to me.
"*Llevatela,*" she says. And I haul it home,
Wondering what I could've done
To deserve such a treasure.

Take 5!

1. Read this poem aloud, noting that it incorporates a few Spanish words that may need a bit of explaining, such as *Doña Pepita* (Mrs. Pepita), *¡Que Chula!* (What a pretty girl!), *calabazita* (zucchini), *¿Que bonita, verdad?* (It's beautiful, isn't it?), and *Llevatela* (Take it). If possible, **invite a Spanish speaker to assist you.**

2. Share the poem again, inviting two students to **pantomime the actions in the garden** while you read the poem aloud.

3. **Talk with students about practical ways to be helpful to older neighbors.**

4. This poem is an example of *free verse*. It doesn't rhyme, but **guide students in seeing how the lines and line breaks build to create a poem.** Talk about how the Spanish words contribute to our understanding of the characters and themes of the poem.

5. A natural companion to this poem is **"Abuelita" by Margarita Engle** (1st Grade, Week 13, page 79), or selections from Juanita Havill's book, *I Heard It from Alice Zucchini: Poems about the Garden.*

Take 5!

1. As you read this poem aloud, **share a favorite trinket, lucky charm, or jingly bracelet,** and pause briefly after each line for emphasis.

2. **Share the poem aloud again, inviting students to say the three middle lines** (*Horses, / Dogs, / A softball glove*) while you read the rest of the lines aloud.

3. *What are some of your favorite lucky charms or special keepsakes?*

4. **Challenge the students to find the pairs of words that demonstrate rhyme (*glove/love*), including "slant" or "almost" rhymes (*wrist/gifts*).** Talk about how the sounds of words and use of rhyme add to the impact of the short lines of the poem. Then read the poem aloud again, emphasizing these words in particular.

5. Follow up with another poem about miniature things, **"Little Village" by Terry Webb Harshman** (3rd Grade, Week 16, page 162), or selections from the e-book *Gift Tag*, edited by Sylvia Vardell and Janet Wong, in which Charles Waters has a poem about a grandfather's pocket watch.

CHARM BRACELET
by **Charles Waters**

On my wrist
Silver gifts

Horses,
Dogs,
A softball glove,

Miniature reminders
Of what I love.

GET A LIFE
by **Eileen Spinelli**

There are books to read.
And birds to feed.
And awesome facts for learning.
There are yards to weed.
And friends in need.
And dreams to set us yearning.
There are trails to hike.
And films to like.
And stories made for swapping.
What I mean to say in this poem today
is there's more to life than
shopping!

Take 5!

1. Prior to sharing the poem, jot numbers on a piece of paper or list on the board (1, 2, 3, etc.) as if you are making a to-do list. Then **read the poem aloud, pausing for a moment after each line.**

2. **Share the poem again, inviting students to join in on the final two lines** (*is there's more to life than / shopping!*) while you read the rest aloud.

3. For discussion: *What are some of your favorite activities to do during holiday breaks?*

4. **Lead students in considering how repeating key words and phrases, particularly at the beginning of each line (*There are; And*), helps build a poem** and can add to the distinctive rhythm of the lines. Then read the poem out loud together again, listening for the patterns.

5. Link this poem with another thoughtful poem by **Eileen Spinelli, "Today"** (4th Grade, Week 29, page 215).

Take 5!

1. Add energy to reading this poem aloud by incorporating motions for key words like *jumped, flew, sailed, urged, hitched, drove, took off, rode, hailed, crawled, slid, hopped, climbed, held, came.* **Note that no verb is repeated!** You may also need to explain words like *yacht, yak,* and *gnu.*

2. Remind the students about all the actions in the poem and then display the poem text. **Invite students to choose their favorite action line and chime in (and pantomime, too) when that line appears,** while you read the whole poem aloud.

3. For discussion: *Which of these modes of transportation would you like to try (if it were possible)?*

4. Talk with students about how **the poet uses exaggeration, or *hyperbole,* in this poem for humorous effect.** Pinpoint examples in the words and phrases the poet uses to create a scene in your mind.

5. Share another poem with a surprise in the final line, also written by **Lesléa Newman,** **"Half-Past Never"** (2nd Grade, Week 26, page 132).

GREETINGS
by **Lesléa Newman**

I jumped aboard a midnight train,
I flew inside a silver plane,
I sailed a thirty-eight foot yacht,
I urged my horse into a trot,
I hitched my wagon to a star,
I drove a brand new racing car,
I took off in a shiny rocket,
I rode inside a giant's pocket,
I hailed a yellow taxi cab,
I crawled along beside a crab,
I slid downhill upon my skis,
I hopped across the tops of trees,
I climbed upon a wooly yak,
I held fast to a possum's back,
I came by subway, bus, and gnu,
Just to say hello to you.

FUNNY BONE (HUMERUS)
by **Michael J. Rosen**

Your upper arm, the humerus,
     has no idea what's funny:
slip on a dropped banana peel,
     invent something punny,
make your hand and armpit squeal—
     how can it tell what's humorous?

Even though your humeri
     have biceps with a belly
they're not for making belly laughs.
     That name is simply silly!
Did someone on the O.R. staff
     think it'd be humorous,

in the midst of a humorless
     dissection, to make a pun
about the bone and how it hurts
     like crazy when you stun
that tender elbow nerve that blurts
     out *PAIN* and, more or less,

turns you into pancake batter?
     That bone's no laughing matter.

Take 5!

1. You may need to introduce the word *humerus* (upper arm bone) before reading this poem aloud. **Pump your arm up as if cheering while reading the first line.**

2. **Share the poem again, inviting students to join in on the final line** (*That bone's no laughing matter*) while you read the rest aloud. Pump your arm again to cue them.

3. For discussion: ***What are some things that you think are humorous?***

4. Poets love to play with words and how they are arranged on the page. **Talk with students about how the words *humorous* and *humerus* are used in this poem and how the poet uses the stanzas and line breaks to create a distinctive rhythm.**

5. Follow up with another poem with a humerus, **"The Guy in the Closet" by Heidi Bee Roemer** (4th Grade, Week 19, page 205), or selections from *The Blood-Hungry Spleen and Other Poems about Our Parts* by Allan Wolf.

FROM ROOT TO TIP
by Carol-Ann Hoyte

My exposed part
that's seen
is biologically
dead protein;
and what's neat
to discover
is I don't ever cover
the palms of your hands
and soles of your feet.

Answer: hair

> ### Take 5!
>
> 1. Before reading this poem aloud, **alert students to listen carefully for clue words** in the details so they can guess the subject of the poem.
>
> 2. **Read the poem again, inviting students to say the four fact-filled lines of the poem (lines 3, 4, 8, and 9) in unison** (*is biologically / dead protein; the palms of your hands / and soles of your feet*) while you read the rest aloud. Cue students by patting the top of your head (if you have hair there!).
>
> 3. **Talk about all the different kinds of hair we have** (brown, blonde, red, curly, straight, etc.).
>
> 4. Reading and writing riddles is a fun way to reinforce nonfiction facts and vocabulary. **Guide students in identifying the clues and details that suggest the poem's subject.**
>
> 5. Connect this poem with another riddle poem by **Carol-Ann Hoyte, "It's a Wrap"** (3rd Grade, Week 19, page 165).

PAINT MIND
by Susan Marie Swanson

I'm painting two friends wearing backpacks,
and they're lacing their shoes for a climb.
Up what?
A ladder?
A mountain?
A tree?
My paint and I get to decide.

Take 5!

1. **Have a paint brush and a big, blank piece of paper handy** before reading the poem aloud.

2. Share the poem again, and **invite students to say lines 4, 5, and 6** (*A ladder? / A mountain? / A tree?*) as you read the rest of the poem aloud.

3. For discussion: *Where would you prefer to go with a friend—mountains, woods, lakes, or deserts?*

4. **Talk with students about how the poet repeats the use of questions to help build the poem** and uses an "almost" or "slant" rhyme at the beginning and end (*climb/decide*) to frame the poem. Then read the poem aloud together again with special emphasis on the question lines in particular.

5. Link this poem with another poem about painting, **"Waiting" by Lorie Ann Grover** (Kindergarten, Week 20, page 46).

Take 5!

1. **Put a copy of this poem in an envelope** and then take it out as if reading a letter when you read this poem aloud.

2. **Invite students to help perform the poem** by reading the final stanza aloud (saying *love* 12 times!) as you read the rest of the poem aloud.

3. **Review the parts of a friendly or personal letter**: greeting (*Dear Human*), body of the letter, closing (*Love*), signature (*Your mutt, Max*), and possible postscript.

4. **Sometimes poets borrow patterns from things like letters to create a poem.** Discuss the details about human-dog relationships that are presented from the dog's point of view in this letter-poem.

5. Follow up with **"My Dog Jack Thinks Up His Valentine" by Patricia Hubbell** (2nd Grade, Week 21, page 127), or choose selections from *Forgive Me, I Meant to Do It: False Apology Poems* by Gail Carson Levine.

YOU MISBEHAVE
by **Gail Carson Levine**

Dear Human,

When you came home today, you let me lick you
and you scratched me behind the ears
for just two minutes before you left
for soccer practice with your real friends.
Then, later, you ate fried chicken and scraped
the bones into the trash where good dogs don't go,
and you filled my bowl with Fido's Friend,
which tastes like mold.

I put up with a lot from you, especially outdoors.
How would you like it if you had to wear a leash
and I hauled on your neck?
And you never let me kill a bird or a squirrel.
When you decide to play, you tie a cape around me
and call me Superdog and make me sit
and roll over until I want to howl from boredom.
You're not all bad.
A few minutes ago you pulled my toy toad
out from under the couch, and I didn't have to bark
at it to get your attention.
If everything you did was up to that high standard,
I'd have no complaints.

Love, love, love, love,
love, love, love, love,
love, love, love, love,
Your mutt Max

THE BULLY
by **Guadalupe Garcia McCall**

She is standing across the street,
Yelling words that sting
Like bees on tender skin.
She is bigger, stronger, tougher.
Mas mala.
I don't know what I did to her,
But I am not afraid.
She can only hurt me if I let her.
My father is watching me from the porch.
His eyes are squinting.
The toothpick in his mouth
Jerks up and down and from side to side,
Like a trigger, as he grits his teeth.
"*Tonta*, you gonna let her
Talk to you like that?" he asks.
I shrug my shoulders and try to walk inside,
But his hand on my shoulder is a command.
He is big, bigger than the girl
Across the street. "*No te dejes,*" he says
"Go over there and knock her teeth in!"
I know there is no way out of this.
I hit her once, on the ear.
Suddenly, she is a windmill,
Pounding the air out of me.
I fall down and scrape my knee
On the pebbled driveway.
The taste of blood scalds
The tip of my tongue and I spit it out.
My father throws his arms up
In the air and stalks away.
She kicks me then and I cry in rage,
Ashamed.

Take 5!

1. This poem incorporates a few Spanish words that may need a bit of prior explanation, such as *Mas mala* (Meaner), *Tonta* (Silly), and *No te dejes* (Don't let this happen to you). If possible, **invite a Spanish speaker to assist you.**

2. **Stage a *tableau*,** a frozen moment of the poem posed as a scene, with volunteers posing as described in the poem—as the girl bully, the protagonist (boy or girl), and the father. Challenge them to pose in three scenes, one from the beginning of the poem, one from the middle, and one at the end as you read the poem aloud.

3. For discussion: *What can you do when you're in a no-win situation?*

4. Poets often compare one thing to another to give us a fresh perspective on both things. **Talk with students about some of the similes and metaphors** in this poem. Use examples such as *Like bees on tender skin; Like a trigger* (similes); *His hand on my shoulder / Is a command; Suddenly, she is a windmill* (metaphors).

5. Match this poem with **"Poem for a Bully" by Eileen Spinelli** (4th Grade, Week 22, page 208).

Take 5!

1. Before reading this poem aloud, **share a map that shows Cuba** as a poetry prop. You might need to give a history mini-lesson and explain the title of the poem.

2. **Share the poem again, displaying the text, and invite students to read the last three lines of the poem** (*filled with family / and dreams / not enemies*).

3. **Invite students to share stories about friends and family in faraway places.**

4. In this lyrical first-person poem, the poet explores emotions and memories. **Guide students in talking about the details that emerge in each stanza,** the feelings the poet expresses, and what themes emerge.

5. Link this poem with another island perspective in **"Saturdays" by Monica Gunning** (4th Grade, Week 14, page 200).

COLD WAR
by **Margarita Engle**

Cold and Cuba
were not words
that I could speak
in the same sentence.

The newsmen failed
to understand
that the island was hot, green,
and beautifully
warm,
friendly,
alive,

filled with family
and dreams
not enemies.

WHEEL OF PROGRESS
by **Juanita Havill**

Before the cart, the horse,
the log before the wheel
transported stones for pyramids
or bison for a meal.

A slice of log, then spokes.
A chariot wheel, how noble!
Add a motor in five thousand years
to make the auto mobile.

Take 5!

1. In this poem, **the poet was inspired to have fun with the expression** *don't put the cart before the horse.* Look and listen for it!

2. **Display the words of the poem and ask for eight volunteers to help read the poem aloud, one volunteer for each line** of the poem. Let them practice their lines softly with a partner, then read the poem aloud together.

3. **Survey students collectively on which of these transportation modes they have experienced** (*cart, horse, log, wheel, car*).

4. Sometimes poets weave facts throughout their poems. **Guide students in noting what information we learn about wheels and transportation from this poem,** and talk about how the lines are arranged to dole out the facts bit by bit.

5. Connect this poem with another fact-filled poem by **Juanita Havill, "Moon Buggy"** (3rd Grade, Week 36, page 182).

Take 5!

1. **Tap a regular rhythm ("drop" or play a beat) while you read this poem aloud.**

2. **Invite students to join you by chanting the *hip / hop* lines,** with a pause between the two words, while you read the rest of the poem aloud.

3. For discussion: ***What are your favorite kinds of music?***

4. Poets give their poems shape and structure in many ways. **Talk with students about how the short lines and line breaks give this poem a distinctive rhythm.** Then read the whole poem aloud together again.

5. Follow up with **"Your Chance to Dance" by Brod Bagert** (1st Grade, Week 25, page 91), Jaime Adoff's book *The Song Shoots Out of My Mouth: A Celebration of Music,* or selections from *Hip Hop Speaks to Children,* edited by Nikki Giovanni.

BEATS ON TOP OF YOUR HEAD
by Jaime Adoff

I've got my
hip
hop
and it's time to
drop
another beat
on top of your head.
Rhythms fall like rain
Rhythms call my name.
I can sing and rap and play and dance
from Dallas, Texas to Paris, France.
I've got my
hip
hop
won't ever stop
droppin' beats on top of your head.
Droppin' beats while you make your bed.
Droppin' beats while you butter your bread.
Droppin' beats until your books are read.
I've got my
hip
hop— don't wanna stop
but I've come to the end of this poem
my friend.

HOW TO OPEN THE ATTIC DOOR
by **April Halprin Wayland**

To open up the attic door,
(to find that old cartoon you drew),
you have to sing a silly tune,
you have to sing it backwards, too
and play it on the noodle flute
while putting on your bathing suit.
And *always* wear blue cowboy boots!

Take 5!

1. If possible, **stand by a door while reading this poem aloud.**

2. Share this humorous poem again and **invite students to choose their favorite line from lines 3-7 and chime in when that line appears** while you read the whole poem aloud.

3. For discussion: **What is the secret in giving clear directions?**

4. This poem is another good example of using both end rhyme and rhyme in the middle, or *internal rhyme.* **Challenge the students to find the words that rhyme, including "almost" or "slant" rhymes** (*cartoon, drew, you, tune, too, noodle, flute, suit, blue, boots*). Read the poem aloud again, emphasizing those words in particular.

5. Link this poem with the nonsensical **"Eight-year-old Uncle" by X. J. Kennedy** (3rd Grade, Week 26, page 172), or share selections from *If You Were a Chocolate Mustache* by J. Patrick Lewis.

Take 5!

1. **Encourage students to close their eyes and imagine a spring morning** with a blue sky, new green grass, and fresh air. Then continue by reading this poem aloud.

2. Next, **divide the students into two groups—one to read the words on the left side of the poem and one to read the words on the right side of the poem.** Read the poem taking turns in a back and forth way. Then try the poem a different way, reading the left side as one poem and the right side as another.

3. For discussion: *What are signs of spring where you live?*

4. **The arrangement of words on a page is very important in poetry, and in this poem it's particularly crucial.** Talk with students about how the word placement adds to the poem's meaning and beauty.

5. Look for other poems written in two parts, such as **"Summer Showers" by Carole Gerber** (2nd Grade, Week 35, page 141), or selections from *Ring of Earth: A Child's Book of Seasons* by Jane Yolen.

FIRST TAKE
by **Jane Yolen**

First take a noun:

grass;

Follow with a verb:

shoots;

Embolden it:

suddenly;

Stretch it:

towards the sky;

And you have a sentence
followed by a period
of time:

spring.

MY SISTER LISETTE
by **Carmen T. Bernier-Grand**

My sister Lisette and I
go to bed at the same time.
I go to bed to sleep.
She goes to bed to read
very scary stories.
There I am sound asleep
and she comes and pries my eyes open.
"Are you dead?" she asks.
"No, I'm not dead," I answer.
"Please, let me sleep."
"No, don't fall asleep," she begs.
"Because, if you fall asleep,
I would think you are dead
and that scares me."
I try to stay awake,
but my eyes close involuntarily.
She pokes me.
"Agh!" I scream, startled awake.
"Quit reading that book!"
"No," she says. "I'm in the best part."
That goes on
until the wee hours of the night.
Then she jumps out of her bed.
She checks underneath her bed.
She checks underneath my bed.
She runs to the closet.
She checks between the hanging clothes,
for ghosts!
When she doesn't find any,
she jumps back into her bed,
covers herself from head to toe
and says, "Turn out the light."
The switch is right by her bed,
but I have to get out of my bed,
and turn out the light,
or she won't let me sleep
the rest of my life.

Take 5!

1. Ask students if they have sisters or brothers who sometimes annoy them. Then **read the poem aloud, using slightly different voices for the two sisters** in the poem.

2. Share the poem aloud again, displaying the words, and **invite two (girl) volunteers to read the lines of the sisters in quotation marks while you read the rest of the poem aloud.** Poet protagonist: lines 9-10, 18-19. Lisette: lines 8, 11-14, 20, 32.

3. For discussion: *What are some of your favorite books that you have read?*

4. Talk with students about how the poet uses a first-person point of view, but **communicates the thoughts of two people through dialogue.**

5. Follow up with another family poem, **"Double the Trouble" by Janet Wong** (2nd Grade, Week 13, page119), excerpts from *The Wild Book* by Margarita Engle, or selections from *Emma Dilemma* by Kristine O'Connell George.

Take 5!

1. Read this poem aloud and **ask students to picture the words and images in their minds while listening.**

2. **Display the words of the poem and ask for four volunteers to help read the poem aloud,** one for each of the first four lines of the poem, as you read the rest of the poem. Let them practice their lines softly with a partner first.

3. For discussion: ***What is a fifth grader like?***

4. In this poem the poet uses *metaphors* to describe a meadow, thunder, a bus, and a desk. **Talk with students about how the two things being compared are alike** (*meadow/ocean, thunder/ drummer, bus/puppy, desk/ robot*).

5. Connect this poem with another rich in metaphor, **"Honey" by J. Patrick Lewis** (3rd Grade, Week 32, page 178).

HOW IS A MEADOW AN OCEAN?
by Laura Purdie Salas

A meadow's an ocean with wild waves of wheat
Thunder's a drummer that's keeping storm's beat

A bus is a puppy that runs down the street
A desk is a robot with round, metal feet

A metaphor's a window that changes our view,
A gift to unwrap something old made brand new

CERBERUS
by **Linda Ashman**

One chest.
One tail.
Four legs.
Four paws.

Six eyes.
Six ears.
Three heads.
Three jaws.

Quick bark.
Gruff growl.
Sharp teeth.
Strong bite.

Good guard?
You bet.
Good pet?
Not quite.

Note: In Greek mythology, Cerberus is a vicious, three-headed dog who guards the gate to the underworld.

Take 5!

1. Before reading this poem aloud, **set the stage by showing an image of Cerberus, the three-headed watchdog from Greek mythology.**

2. **Share the poem aloud again with students chiming in for two lines in the final stanza—** *You bet* and *Not quite*—while you read the rest of the poem aloud.

3. For discussion: ***What other characters from Greek mythology do you know?***

4. Poets love to play with words and how they are arranged on the page. **Here the poem is almost like a list with short lines of two syllables each.** Invite students to tap the rhythm of the poem as you share it again. Like a composer with the notes of a song, poets give their poems a beat, too.

5. Share another poem about an unlikely, impossible pet, **"My Pet" by David L. Harrison** (2nd Grade, Week 4, page 110).

Take 5!

1. Survey students about their mice experiences before you read the poem. **Have they ever seen mice in their homes or at a pet store?**

2. **Read the poem aloud again and invite students to say the opening (*Silky*) and closing (*River*) lines** while you read the rest of the poem.

3. For discussion: *Why are people so afraid of such a tiny creature?*

4. There are many special forms of poems that poets like to try. **This poem is written in the form of a *cinquain*, a five-line poem** with one topic that is generally arranged in lines with syllable counts of 2-4-6-8-2 (often with emphasis on the last two syllables). Note: as with other syllabic forms such as haiku and tanka, not all poets restrict themselves to syllable counting. Discuss the details the poet provides about the *house mouse* in this poem.

5. Connect this poem with another cinquain poem by **Laura Purdie Salas, "Fire"** (1st Grade, Week 14, page 80).

HOUSE MOUSE
by **Laura Purdie Salas**

Silky
Whisper-grey mouse
Hesitates, sniffs, trembles—
Surges forward, a quicksilver
River

NIGHT COMES
by **Deborah Chandra**

Night
comes
slow,
as the world
fills up
with cool
milk
from the moon's
tipped cup.

Night
comes
slow,
circles round,
closer . . .
     closer . . .
settling down—
like a big black
cat
with fur of silk,
and deep dark purr,
lapping
the milk.

Take 5!

1. Before sharing this poem, **take a moment to help students picture the day turning to night, the dark sky, the moon shining.** Then continue by reading this poem aloud.

2. **Share the poem again, inviting students to slowly say the repeated lines *Night / comes / slow* (lines 1, 2, 3 and lines 10, 11, 12) as you read the rest of the poem aloud—slowly.**

3. For discussion: *What are the best and worst things about the night?*

4. What comparisons does the poet make in this poem? **Help students identify the *similes* and *metaphors* in the poem** (e.g., *like a big black / cat; as the world / fills up / with cool / milk*).

5. Follow up with **"Poem Like the Sea" by Patricia Hubbell** (3rd Grade, Week 29, page 175), or selections from *Sky Magic,* edited by Lee Bennett Hopkins.

Take 5!

1. In this poem, **the poet plays with the expression *things are looking up*, sharing some unusual examples of things with eyes for "looking."** Read the poem aloud with pauses between each stanza.

2. Share the poem aloud again, displaying the words, if possible. **Invite students to join in on the final stanza.**

3. For discussion: *What might ears of corn "hear" or the mouth of a river "eat?"*

4. Once again, a poet gives human qualities to things that are not human (*personification*). **Guide the students in identifying the key words or lines in the poem that humanize the potato, needles, and shoes.** Then share the poem aloud again.

5. Revisit another poem full of personification, **"My Carrots Are Angry" by Jack Prelutsky** (2nd Grade, Week 33, page 139), or selections from Heidi Mordhorst's book, *Pumpkin Butterfly: Poems from the Other Side of Nature.*

"THINGS ARE LOOKING UP"
by Heidi Mordhorst

Things
like needles, potatoes and lace-up shoes
are turning their eyes to the . . . skies?

Perhaps potatoes are content to gaze up
out of the soil or
out of the darkness of root cellar or
cupboard under the sink
into greenish ground-level daylight.

Maybe needles push sharply up
spinning on their points,
seeking a better view of the unstrung world,
but something like a loose lash
keeps getting in the way.

The shoe has a better chance: looking up
with eyes so small
as to be eyelets, laced together
into a net of eyes. They catch
blurred glimpses, cuffs and knees.

When things
are looking up,
what do they see?

DIRECTIONS
by **Janet Wong**

Turn left at First Ave.
Go straight one mile.
Turn right at Cedar St.
Follow that a while.
Left at Lake Blvd.
Make a U at Maple Rd.

We're here. Now switch
to Vacation Mode!

Take 5!

1. While you share this poem aloud, **walk around the room reading the poem like directions,** turning left, right, and so on as the poem specifies.

2. **Share the poem again, inviting students to chime in on the words** *We're here* as you read the rest of the poem aloud.

3. For discussion: *If you could go anywhere on a vacation, where would you like to go*?

4. Show how **rhyming words help turn this list of directions and abbreviations into a poem** (*mile/while, Rd./Mode*). Poets can create poetry out of nearly anything! This is sometimes called *found poetry*—making a poem out of words, phrases, or sentences from other sources, like directions.

5. Connect this poem with **"Car Trip" by Juanita Havill** (3rd Grade, Week 34, page 180), selections from *Behind the Wheel: Poems about Driving* by Janet Wong, or poems from *The Arrow Finds Its Mark: A Book of Found Poems*, edited by Georgia Heard.

Take 5!

1. As a poetry prop for sharing this poem, **have a suitcase or backpack handy while you read the poem aloud.**

2. **Share the poem again and invite students to chime in on the last two lines of the poem** (*The only problem is that we've / forgotten where we're going!*). Read the rest of the poem aloud, starting slowly, accelerating speed as you go, and then pausing before the final stanza.

3. For discussion: *What is the one item you feel like you can't leave behind when packing for a trip?*

4. Poets give their poems shape in many ways. **Here the poem is made up of four-line stanzas,** or *quatrains*. Talk with students about each stanza and what it adds to the poem. What details tell you the poem is humorous?

5. Match this poem with the acrostic poem **"Family Vacation" by Kathi Appelt** (4th Grade, Week 35, page 221), the packing poem **"By the Sea" by Lesléa Newman** (1st Grade, Week 35, page 101), or selections from *Vacation: We're Going to the Ocean!* by David L. Harrison.

FAMILY VACATION
by **Allan Wolf**

I started packing Monday
when I gathered up my shirts.
My sister packed away a blouse,
a hairbrush, and three skirts.

Daddy packed his razor
and his woolen dress-up slacks.
Mother packed her flowered dress
and a box of crunchy snacks.

We gathered up a couple lamps
and a box of dictionaries,
we even took Sir William
and Bernice, our pet canaries,

the sofa and the kitchen sink,
my old, stuffed Teddy Bear,
the television, bicycles,
Great Grandma's rocking chair!

By Friday we had taken
all the things we had to take.
We even took some things
we really needed by mistake.

We're ready for vacation now,
with all the stuff we're towing.
The only problem is that we've
forgotten where we're going!

WHEN THE FUTURE ARRIVES
by **Bobbi Katz**

When the future arrives,
   breathless,
      immense,
it completely
takes over
the present tense.

Take 5!

1. **Add a bit of fun to sharing this poem with a poetry prop**— perhaps a handful of fortune cookies that you can crack open (in an attempt to find a good fortune)—and then read the poem aloud slowly.

2. **Share the poem again, inviting students to say lines 2 and 3 (*breathless; immense*) in two groups, one group per line,** as you read the rest of the poem aloud.

3. **Invite students to create a time capsule to take with them** to the next grade (in middle school) and to open in a year. Include a favorite poem from this year or from all their elementary school years.

4. Poets love to play with words. Sometimes they'll use a word just because they like the sound of it or because they like the way a word makes a picture in your mind. Sometimes they try **a play on words,** as in this case. Talk with students about how *present tense* can mean more than one thing in this poem.

5. Link this poem with **"The Secret Seed" by Allan Wolf** (2nd Grade, Week 36, page 142) or selections from *Once Around the Sun* by Bobbi Katz.

THE LAST DAY OF SCHOOL
by Deborah Ruddell

The bell sounds, as the kids sweep
through the big doors, and the horns beep,
as the birds cheer in the blue light,
and the bright white
butterflies
skywrite

Summer

ABOUT THE POETS

Biographical information, photos, and lists of some of the published titles of each of our contributing poets can be found at our website, www.PomeloBooks.com. Younger children might like to know, for instance, that Jack Prelutsky collects frog miniatures and April Halprin Wayland was once an aqua farmer!

Most poets have their own websites, too, where you can find contact info for them as well as news about their books and links to their blogs. Some particularly useful poets' blogs are listed in the Poetry Resources section of this book.

If you identified "favorite poets" when reading the poems in this anthology, you might want to contact them about speaking at your school —either in person or via video chat—or participating in a conference for teachers. Some poets enjoy large assemblies, some prefer small workshops, and some do both. Contact them and start a conversation!

MORE POETRY RESOURCES

*"Poetry touches our inner core and invites us into the poem. But to do this, **teachers need to know how to select good poetry**, how best to make poetry available in their classrooms, and when and how to connect it to their lessons."*

৪৩ Kathryn Button ৩৪

Building Your Own Poetry Library

How do we identify which poetry books are the best for children or most useful in the K-5 classroom? One of the best ways to begin is by looking at poetry award winners.

The **Children's Poet Laureate** (CPL) was established by the Poetry Foundation in 2006 to raise awareness of the fact that children have a natural receptivity to poetry and are its most appreciative audience, especially when poems are written specifically for them. The Children's Poet Laureate serves as a consultant to the Foundation and gives public readings. The first CPL was Jack Prelutsky, followed by Mary Ann Hoberman, J. Patrick Lewis, and Kenn Nesbitt.

Another major award for poetry for children is **the National Council of Teachers of English (NCTE) Award for Excellence in Poetry for Children**, given to a poet for her or his entire body of work in writing or anthologizing poetry for children. Several of the winners are included in this anthology: Arnold Adoff, X.J. Kennedy, Nikki Grimes, and J. Patrick Lewis. Any book of poetry by one of these award winners will be worthwhile.

Your Poetry Checklist

☑ Highlight poetry books on the chalk rail, a red wagon, or a table

☑ Seek out poetry books from diverse perspectives

☑ Link poems with picture books, novels, and nonfiction

☑ Connect children's poetry with social studies, science, and mathematics

☑ **Tell your colleagues about Poetry Friday!**

Other prominent awards include The **Lee Bennett Hopkins Award** for Children's Poetry, which is presented annually to an American poet or anthologist for the most outstanding new book of children's poetry published in the previous year; the **Claudia Lewis Award,** given by Bank Street College for the best poetry book of the year; and **The Lion and the Unicorn Award** for Excellence in North American Poetry for the best poetry book published in either the U.S. or Canada. A detailed listing of major poetry awards, past winners, and useful award-related web site links can be found in *The Poetry Teacher's Book of Lists* by Sylvia Vardell.

The Poetry Teacher's Book of Lists also offers input on selecting poetry for young people ages 0-18. It contains 155 different lists and cites nearly 1500 poetry books in a variety of categories including:

- Poetry Awards and "Best" Lists

- Seasonal and Holiday Poetry Booklists (Valentine's Day, Earth Day, Halloween, etc.)

- Multicultural and International Poetry Booklists (such as African American or bilingual poetry books)

- Thematic or Topical Poetry Booklists (humor, family, friendship, coping, etc.)

- Poetry Booklists Across the Curriculum (animals, food, math, science, history, etc.)

- Poetry Booklists Highlighting the Form of Poetry (limericks, acrostics, haiku, etc.)

- Strategies for Creating a Poetry-Friendly Environment (poetry displays and quotes, lesson plan tips, a poetry scavenger hunt, poet birthdays)

- Strategies for Sharing and Responding to Poetry Out Loud (poetry performance tips, assessment rubrics, discussion prompts)

- Strategies for Teaching Poetry Writing (books with poet commentary, poetry written by children, lists of poem forms, writers' checklists)

- General Poetry Teaching Resources (poetry web sites and blogs, poetry text sets, reference tools)

If you are looking for poetry books for Mother's Day or for poems for a unit on insects and bugs, for example, you'll find lists for each of those and more.

Children's Poetry Web Sites and Blogs

As we look for new places for poetry to pop up, you can be sure that this includes the Internet. There are several hundred web sites and blogs that make poems available; these often include audio and video recordings of poets reading their poems and/or biographical information about poets, too. A comprehensive list of poetry websites and blogs can be found in *The Poetry Teacher's Book of Lists* as well as on Sylvia Vardell's Poetry for Children blog.

Most of the established poetry blogs participate in the "Poetry Friday" celebration by posting a poem or poetry-related content on Fridays. Some include teaching activities and even welcome child participation. Sites and blogs also offer links to additional poetry resources on the web. Here is a select list of electronic resources that are particularly helpful in sharing poetry with children.

25 Children's Poetry Web Sites and Blogs You Need to Know

About Poetry:

Alphabet Soup
by Jama Rattigan
JamaRattigan.com

The Academy of American Poets
Poets.org

Favorite Poem Project
FavoritePoem.org

Giggle Poetry
GigglePoetry.com

The Miss Rumphius Effect
by Tricia Stohr-Hunt
MissRumphiusEffect.Blogspot.com

Poetry Alive
PoetryAlive.com

Poetry for Children
by Sylvia Vardell
PoetryForChildren.Blogspot.com

Poetry Foundation
PoetryFoundation.org

Poetry at Play: Poetry Advocates for Children and Young Adults
PoetryatPlay.org

Potato Hill Poetry
Potatohill.com

Wild Rose Reader
by Elaine Magliaro
WildRoseReader.Blogspot.com

Wordswimmer by Bruce Black
Wordswimmer.Blogspot.com

A Year of Reading
by Franki Sibberson
and Mary Lee Hahn
ReadingYear.Blogspot.com

Poets:

April Halprin Wayland
AprilHalprinWayland.com

Bookjoy
by Pat Mora
ShareBookjoy.Blogspot.com

David L. Harrison's Blog
DavidLHarrison.Wordpress.com

The Drift Record
by Julie Larios
JulieLarios.Blogspot.com

Father Goose
by Charles Ghigna
CharlesGhigna.Blogspot.com

Florian Café
by Douglas Florian
FlorianCafe.Blogspot.com

GottaBook
by Greg Pincus
Gottabook.Blogspot.com

Nikki Sounds Off
by Nikki Grimes
NikkiGrimes.com/blog

The Poem Farm
by Amy Ludwig VanDerwater
PoemFarm.AmyLV.com

Poetry for Kids
by Kenn Nesbitt
Poetry4Kids.com

Poetry Suitcase
by Janet Wong
PoetrySuitcase.com

Writing the World for Kids
by Laura Purdie Salas
LauraSalas.com/blog

E-Resources for Poetry Teaching

One of the most controversial topics in the world of reading today concerns e-books. Some people think that e-books will replace paper books and change the way we read—and they're afraid of those changes. We agree that changes will happen, but we're excited by the possibilities. Consider:

- a teacher can read a book review at lunch and buy an e-book version of it (for less than the price of lunch);

- that book might be a collection of poems from Mexico or Australia but is delivered immediately without shipping costs or customs fees;

- the teacher can download the e-book onto an e-reader and also a regular computer that can be projected onto a screen for the whole class to read aloud together;

- e-resources are easily searchable. A teacher can look for a poem using keywords like *family* or *armadillo*. Even if you prefer paper books, you might consider owning a second copy that is digital as a teaching resource;

- and reluctant readers (who might not like paper books but might enjoy manipulating text on a screen) can read the book using electronic bookmarks, a glossary, and sometimes read-aloud features, too.

Poetry is particularly well-suited to e-books. Imagine: a second grader is standing in line at the post office with his mother. He is bored. His mother hands him her cell phone. To play a video game? No: to read a poem in an e-book. He reads the short poem to himself and likes it. Then he reads it again —as he's been taught—aloud. His mother laughs. The woman standing behind him laughs. He reads another poem aloud and directs his mother (in a second reading) to chime in and guess the rhyming word. The man in front of him turns around to say the rhyming words. Next thing they know, the boy and his mother are first in line and bursting with the joy of reading.

If you want to try an e-book and need to know where to get started, you'll find some titles and resources here:

PoetryFridayAnthology.Blogspot.com

PoetryTagTime.Blogspot.com

TeenPoetryTagTime.Blogspot.com

PoetryGiftTag.Blogspot.com

PoetryforChildren.Blogspot.com

PoetryTeachersBookofLists.Blogspot.com

Professional Resource Books

This abbreviated list of professional reference sources will provide additional background that you will find helpful in selecting and sharing poetry with young people. **For further reading, you will find several dozen professional resources listed in** *The Poetry Teacher's Book of Lists.*

Bauer, Caroline Feller. *The Poetry Break: An Annotated Anthology with Ideas for Introducing Children to Poetry.*

Booth, David and Moore, Bill. *Poems Please! Sharing Poetry with Children.*

Chatton, Barbara. *Using Poetry Across the Curriculum.*

Collom, Jack and Noethe, Sheryl. *Poetry Everywhere: Teaching Poetry Writing in School and in the Community.*

Fitch, Sheree and Swartz, Larry. *The Poetry Experience: Choosing and Using Poetry in the Classroom.*

Franco, Betsy. *Conversations with a Poet: Inviting Poetry into K-12 Classrooms.*

Heard, Georgia. *Awakening the Heart: Exploring Poetry in Elementary and Middle School.*

Holbrook, Sara. *Practical Poetry: A Nonstandard Approach to Meeting Content-Area Standards.*

Holbrook, Sara and Salinger, Michael. *Outspoken: How to Improve Writing and Speaking through Poetry Performance.*

Hopkins, Lee Bennett. *Pass the Poetry, Please.*

Janeczko, Paul B. *Reading Poetry in the Middle Grades: 20 Poems and Activities that Meet the Common Core Standards and Cultivate a Passion for Poetry.*

Kennedy, X. J. and Kennedy, Dorothy. *Knock at a Star.*

Livingston, Myra Cohn. *Poem-Making.*

McClure, Amy. *Sunrises and Songs: Reading and Writing Poetry in the Elementary Classroom.*

Partington, Richie. *I Second that Emotion: Sharing Children's and Young Adult Poetry: A 21st Century Guide for Teachers and Librarians.*

Sloan, Glenna. *Give Them Poetry: A Guide for Sharing Poetry with Children K-8.*

Stanley, Nile. *Creating Readers with Poetry.*

Thomas, Joseph T., Jr. *Poetry's Playground: The Culture of Contemporary American Children's Poetry.*

Treviño, Rose Z. *Read Me a Rhyme in Spanish and English.*

Vardell, Sylvia M. *Poetry Aloud Here: Sharing Poetry with Children.*

Vardell, Sylvia M. *Poetry People: A Practical Guide to Children's Poets.*

Vardell, Sylvia M. *The Poetry Teacher's Book of Lists.*

A Mini Glossary of Poetry Terms

It can be helpful to have a vocabulary for discussing poetry, but please don't let this aspect get in the way of enjoying poems. This is a short list of key terms used throughout the Take 5 activities.

Alliteration: The repetition of consonants for effect, particularly as the initial sound in a string of words

Couplet: Paired lines of verses, often rhyming

Free verse: Poetry that does not follow a set pattern or form and is usually irregular in line length

Haiku: A three-line poem of Japanese origin and usually about nature. The first and third lines generally have five syllables and the second line has seven.

Image: Words invoking or describing sensory perceptions; *imagery* is the collective term for images

Internal rhyme: The rhyming words within a line of poetry

Lyrical poem: Literally meaning "to be sung accompanied by the lyre"; *lyric* has come to mean a poem expressing the poet's emotions; some poets use the term "in the lyrical voice" to describe first-person poems full of reflection

Metaphor: A figure of speech in which one thing or idea is represented by implicit comparison with another

Meter: The pattern of stressed and unstressed syllables in verse that creates a distinctive rhythm

Narrative poem: A poem that tells a story, often in third person

Onomatopoeia: Words that capture the sounds they describe

Personification: Describing non-human things in human terms

Quatrain: A four-line stanza

Repetition: Sounds, words, phrases, or structures used again and again in a poem, usually for musical effect or enhanced meaning

Rhyme: The matching of syllable sounds at the ends of lines of verse

Rhythm: The pattern of beats or stresses in a line of poetry that conveys a sense of movement or sound

Simile: An explicit comparison between two things or ideas, usually using "as" or "like"

Stanza: A group of poetic lines often repeated according to a fixed pattern throughout a poem

Tanka: A five-line poem derived from the Japanese tradition, generally syllable pattern of 5-7-5-7-7

Tercet: A three-line stanza

INDEX AND CREDITS

Copyright & Permissions

For permission to reprint any of the poems in this book, please contact the individual poets listed here either directly or through their agents.

Most of these poets can be reached through their individual web sites, which are listed at our Pomelo Books web site, www.pomelobooks.com. If you need help getting in touch with a poet, just let us know and we'll be happy to connect you.

A note on copyright:

If it doesn't feel right to copy it . . .
please *don't!*

Poets (like plumbers and lawyers and teachers and acrobats) need to earn a living from their work; permissions fees and royalties help pay the rent!

Title Index

A

Abuelita 79
Africa's Child 129
After Sledding 123
All Worn Out 111
Animal Talk 53
Antarctica, Antarctic*O*! 89
Apprehended by Autumn 235
Appy Birthday 130
Archeology of a Book 214
Armadillo 92
Avocado 197

B

Baby Tooth 84
Backpack 228
Backyard Swing 118
Bailes 203
Barnyard Ballet 171
Bat 74
Beats on Top of Your Head 251
Bird Alert: Storm Warning! 194
Bluebirds 154
Bluejay Sings Two Different Songs 34
Book, The 54
Bouncing Along 60
Branch of Friendship, A 207
Breakfast Boss, The 159
Bubble Bath 41
Bubble Gum 121
Bully, The 248
By the Sea 101

C

Cabbage House 38
Car Trip 180
Catching a Yawn 164

Catku 177
Centipede 222
Centipede's Excuse, A 100
Cerberus 256
Charm Bracelet 241
Christmas Is 122
Clam, A 153
Clay Time 86
Cold War 249
Corn, Before the Butter 217
Crayons 57
Crocodile (Chandra) 218
Crocodile (Paul) 73
Crossing the International
    Date Line 220
Crunch 116

D

Directions 260
Do Kind, The 167
Dog Walking Tanka 137
Doña Pepita 240
Double the Trouble 119
Dreamland 125

E

Earthworms 232
Eight-year-old Uncle 172
Elders Told Me, The 213
Embarrassed 88
Equipment Haiku 229
Explorer 169

F

Family Vacation (Appelt) 221
Family Vacation (Wolf) 261
Feeling Jumpy 187

Fifty Yard Dash 188

Fire! 80

Fire Station 120

First 94

First Take 253

Fish 70

Fishing 149

Flapjack Flip 237

Flat Gray Rock 152

Forgive and Forget 128

Frog and Toad 47

From Root to Tip 245

Front Yard Where the Maple Tree
    Stands, The 198

Funday, Imaginary 1st 147

Funny Bone (Humerus) 244

G

Get a Life 242

Gift Ungiven 202

Give Me Wings 209

Global Gorging 196

Gnat and Flea 93

Good Dog! Bad Dog! 231

Grandfather's Chopsticks 77

Green Sea Turtle 233

Greetings 243

Guy in the Closet, The 205

H

Half-Past Never 132

Happy Song for the First Day
    of School 27

Honey 178

House Mouse 257

How Big Is the Atlas Moth? 114

How Is a Meadow an Ocean? 255

How Many Slams Are in an Old
    Screen Door? 52

How the Birds Got Their Colors 166

How the Geese Became Chiefs
    of the Birds 234

How to Open the Attic Door 252

Humpback Whale 193

I

I Had to Get a Shot at the Doctor's 204

I Might Go to Mars 134

I Sit On My Bottom 45

Ingredients for a Valentine 87

It's a Wrap 165

I've Never Seen a Purple Cow 206

K

Kangarooster, The 216

Kerchoo! 85

Keys 51

Kindergarten Kid 28

L

Last Day of School, The 263

Last Try 97

Let's Hop Around Like Kangaroos 29

Library, The 107

Litter's Littlest 71

Little Village 162

Lizard and Chameleon 126

Look It Up! 173

Loose Tooth, Whose Tooth? 56

Lucky Penny 161

M

Momma's Trying 124

Moon Buggy 182

Most Glad-to-See Day of the Year, The 21

Moving Up Day 62

Mrs. Betty 40

Mud Supper 81

Music Lesson 131

My Best Friend Is Leaving 181

My Bike 58

My Carrots Are Angry 139

My Dog 75

My Dog Jack Thinks Up His Valentine 127

My Kindergarten Choir 42

My Kitchen Was Invaded 158

My Noisy Family 163

My Pet 110

My Porcupine Is Feeling Fine 190

My Sister Lisette 254

My Tree House 78

N

Night Comes 258

No Way! 61

No Wonder 59

O

Oh Man! 31

Once a Week at Noon 96

Ostrich, The 192

Out My Window 160

Outer Spaceman 138

P

Paint Mind 246

Petting Zoo 30

Photo Op 82

Pick-Up Truck 140

Pirate Parrot 191

Plague of Penguins, A 150

Poem a Day, A 95

Poem for a Bully 208

Poem Like the Sea 175

Poems Are Out of This World 55

Pumpkin 157

Q

A Quiet Day 174

R

Ready 67

Real Bed, A 238

Recess (Harley) 108

Recess (Krueger) 148

Recipe for a Poem 135

Riddle 201

Rodeo 69

Rough and Tumble 136

Running Back 189

S

Sack Lunch 37

Saturdays 200

Secret of the Clouds, The 99

Secret Seed, The 142

See-Saw 98

Skype 90

Small Talk 168

Snack Rules 76

Something I Did 48

Spanish Ears 133

Spotty's Tongue 151

Stapler 179

Star-Nosed Mole, The 113

Stormy Day 43

Summer Showers 141

Summer Storm 219

Super Key Man 210

T

Tadpole Wishes 33

Taste of Taco, A 117

Teddy Wear 35

They Call It "Science" 50

"Things are looking up" 259

Today 215

Tomato Sandwiches 236

Tooth 44

Tree I Leaned Against 72

Trouble on the Trail 49

Two Scoops 156

U

Underwear Scare 68

V

Vacation 102

Vacation Communication 170

W

Waiting (Grover) 46

Waiting (Grimes) 239

Watching Football 83

Way You Sound, The 199

What's the Opposite . . . 230

Wheel of Progress 250

When the Future Arrives 262

When the Rain Falls 195

Who Invented Cookies? 36

Who's Who 39

Why Does Weather? 115

Why Hippos Look Baked 212

Winner, The 109

Wondering 155

Woodland Vole, The 112

World's Most Ancient Ant, The 32

World's Most Intelligent Chicken, The 227

Writer's Drill, The 176

Y

You Misbehave 247

You Think This Is A Dance 211

Your Chance to Dance 91

Poet Index

A

Acey, Joy 51, 70
Adoff, Arnold 152, 211
Adoff, Jaime 251
Appelt, Kathi 221, 236
Ashman, Linda 192, 256
Atkins, Jeannine 171, 231

B

Bagert, Brod 91
Bernier-Grand, Carmen T. 133, 254
Black, Robyn Hood 49, 76
Brown, Susan Taylor 195
Bruchac, Joseph 166, 213, 234
Bryant, Jen 154, 229
Bulion, Leslie 113

C

Calmenson, Stephanie 28, 50, 54, 95
Chandra, Deborah 218, 258
Cotten, Cynthia 85, 155

D

Dempsey, Kristy 60, 69, 100, 111, 135, 235
Denton, Graham 35, 98, 209
Dotlich, Rebecca Kai 40, 43, 117

E

Engle, Margarita 79, 137, 249

F

Franco, Betsy 123, 151, 214

G

Gerber, Carole 141
Ghigna, Charles 53, 55, 78
Graham, Joan Bransfield 36, 67, 169, 220
Grandits, John 199

Grimes

Grimes, Nikki 201, 239
Grover, Lorie Ann 46, 188
Gunning, Monica 200, 238

H

Hahn, Mary Lee 34
Harley, Avis 42, 71, 97, 108, 164, 207
Harrison, David L. 31, 61, 110
Harshman, Terry Webb 33, 38, 68, 86, 162, 196
Havill, Juanita 134, 180, 182, 250
Heard, Georgia 109, 179
Hershenhorn, Esther 176, 210
Holbrook, Sara 41, 107, 120
Hoyte, Carol-Ann 165, 170, 245
Hubbell, Patricia 27, 127, 175, 187

J

Jules, Jacqueline 88, 189

K

Katz, Bobbi 87, 262
Kennedy, X.J. 74, 92, 118, 172
Krueger, Michele 148

L

Larios, Julie 39, 58, 138, 150, 191
Latham, Irene 219, 228
Lawson, JonArno 202
Levine, Gail Carson 247
Levy, Constance 59, 161, 194, 197
Levy, Debbie 116, 181
Lewis, J. Patrick 47, 93, 126, 178, 212
Lyon, George Ella 72, 122

M

McCall, Guadalupe Garcia 203, 240, 248
Mordhorst, Heidi 147, 259

N

Nesbitt, Kenn 190

Newman, Lesléa 101, 132, 136, 206, 243

P

Park, Linda Sue 82, 156

Paul, Ann Whitford 57, 73, 230

Pincus, Greg 94, 121

Prelutsky, Jack 32, 96, 139, 153, 158, 216, 227

Q

Quattlebaum, Mary 81, 115

R

Roemer, Heidi Bee 89, 173, 205, 237

Rosen, Michael J. 222, 232, 244

Ruddell, Deborah 114, 263

S

Salas, Laura Purdie 30, 80, 131, 217, 255, 257

Salinger, Michael 45, 163

Slesarik, Ken 112, 168

Spinelli, Eileen 208, 215, 242

Swanson, Susan Marie 246

V

VanDerwater, Amy Ludwig 44, 84, 102, 160, 174

W

Wardlaw, Lee 177

Waters, Charles 37, 75, 241

Wayland, April Halprin 130, 204, 252

Weatherford, Carole Boston 56, 125, 129

Withrow, Steven 233

Wolf, Allan 21, 29, 52, 99, 142, 198, 261

Wong, Janet 48, 62, 77, 83, 90, 119, 124, 128, 140, 149, 159, 167, 260

Y

Yolen, Jane 157, 193, 253

Poem Credits

Joy Acey: "Keys" (Kindergarten, Week 25: Song & Dance), "Fish" (1st Grade, Week 4: Pets); copyright ©2012 by Joy Acey. Used with permission of the author. All rights reserved.

Arnold Adoff: "Flat Gray Rock" (3rd Grade, Week 6: On the Ground), "You Think This Is A Dance" (4th Grade, Week 25: Song & Dance); copyright ©2012 by Arnold Adoff. Used with permission of the author. All rights reserved.

Jaime Adoff: "Beats on Top of Your Head" (5th Grade, Week 25: Song & Dance); copyright ©2012 by Jaime Adoff. Used with permission of the author. All rights reserved.

Kathi Appelt: "Family Vacation" (4th Grade, Week 35: Summer Vacation), "Tomato Sandwiches" (5th Grade, Week 10: Food); copyright ©2012 by Kathi Appelt. Used with permission of the author. All rights reserved.

Linda Ashman: "The Ostrich" (4th Grade, Week 6: On the Ground), "Cerberus" (5th Grade, Week 30: Rhyme, Repetition, & Rhythm); copyright ©2012 by Linda Ashman. Used with permission of the author. All rights reserved.

Jeannine Atkins: "Barnyard Ballet" (3rd Grade, Week 25: Song & Dance), "Good Dog! Bad Dog!" (5th Grade, Week 5: More Pets); copyright ©2012 by Jeannine Atkins. Used with permission of the author. All rights reserved.

Brod Bagert: "Your Chance to Dance" (1st Grade, Week 25: Song & Dance); copyright ©2012 by Brod Bagert. Used with permission of the author. All rights reserved.

Carmen T. Bernier-Grand: "Spanish Ears" (2nd Grade, Week 27: World of Words), "My Sister Lisette" (5th Grade, Week 28: Books); copyright ©2012 by Carmen T. Bernier-Grand. Used with permission of the author. All rights reserved.

Robyn Hood Black: "Trouble on the Trail" (Kindergarten, Week 23: Exploring), "Snack Rules" (1st Grade, Week 10: Food); copyright ©2012 by Robyn Hood Black. Used with permission of the author. All rights reserved.

Susan Taylor Brown: "When the Rain Falls" (4th Grade, Week 9: Weather); copyright ©2012 by Susan Taylor Brown. Used with permission of the author. All rights reserved.

Joseph Bruchac: "How the Birds Got Their Colors" (3rd Grade, Week 20: Art & Colors), "The Elders Told Me" (4th Grade, Week 27: World of Words), "How the Geese Became Chiefs of the Birds" (5th Grade, Week 8: In the Air); copyright ©2012 by Joseph Bruchac. Used with permission of the author. All rights reserved.

Jen Bryant: "Bluebirds" (3rd Grade, Week 8: In the Air), "Equipment Haiku" (5th Grade, Week 3: Fun & Games); copyright ©2012 by Jen Bryant. Used with permission of the author. All rights reserved.

Leslie Bulion: "The Star-Nosed Mole" (2nd Grade, Week 7: In the Water); copyright ©2012 by Leslie Bulion. Used with permission of the author. All rights reserved.

Stephanie Calmenson: "Kindergarten Kid" (Kindergarten, Week 2: More School), "They Call It 'Science'" (Kindergarten, Week 24: Science & Technology), "The Book" (Kindergarten, Week 28: Books), "A Poem a Day" (1st Grade, Week 29: Poetry Poems); copyright ©2012 by Stephanie Calmenson. Used with permission of the author. All rights reserved.

Deborah Chandra: "Crocodile" (4th Grade, Week 32: Metaphor & Simile), "Night Comes" (5th Grade, Week 32: Metaphor & Simile); copyright ©2012 by Deborah Chandra. Used with permission of the author. All rights reserved.

Cynthia Cotten: "Kerchoo!" (1st Grade, Week 19: More Human Body), "Wondering" (3rd Grade, Week 9: Weather); copyright ©2012 by Cynthia Cotten. Used with permission of the author. All rights reserved.

Kristy Dempsey: "Bouncing Along" (Kindergarten, Week 34: On the Move), "Rodeo" (1st Grade, Week 3: Fun & Games), "A Centipede's Excuse" (1st Grade, Week 34: On the Move), "All Worn Out" (2nd Grade, Week 5: More Pets), "Recipe for a Poem" (2nd Grade, Week 29: Poetry Poems), "Apprehended by Autumn" (5th Grade, Week 9: Weather); copyright ©2012 by Kristy Dempsey. Used with permission of the author. All rights reserved.

Graham Denton: "Teddy Wear" (Kindergarten, Week 9: Weather), "See-Saw" (1st Grade, Week 32: Metaphor & Simile), "Give Me Wings" (4th Grade, Week 23: Exploring); copyright ©2012 by Graham Denton. Used with permission of the author. All rights reserved.

Rebecca Kai Dotlich: "Mrs. Betty" (Kindergarten, Week 14: Community), "Stormy Day" (Kindergarten, Week 17: Time Together), "A Taste of Taco" (2nd Grade, Week 11: More Food); copyright ©2012 by Rebecca Kai Dotlich. Used with permission of Curtis Brown, Ltd. All rights reserved.

Margarita Engle: "Abuelita" (1st Grade, Week 13: Families), "Dog-Walking Tanka" (2nd Grade, Week 31: Different Forms), "Cold War" (5th Grade, Week 23: Exploring); copyright ©2012 by Margarita Engle. Used with permission of the author. All rights reserved.

Betsy Franco: "After Sledding" (2nd Grade, Week 17: Time Together), "Spotty's Tongue" (3rd Grade, Week 5: More Pets), "Archeology of a Book" (4th Grade, Week 28: Books); copyright ©2012 by Betsy Franco. Used with permission of the author. All rights reserved.

Carole Gerber: "Summer Showers" (2nd Grade, Week 35: Summer Vacation); copyright ©2012 by Carole Gerber. Used with permission of the author. All rights reserved.

Charles Ghigna: "Animal Talk" (Kindergarten, Week 27: World of Words), "Poems Are Out of This World" (Kindergarten, Week 29: Poetry Poems), "My Tree House" (1st Grade, Week 12: House & Home); copyright ©2012 by Charles Ghigna. Used with permission of the author. All rights reserved.

Joan Bransfield Graham: "Who Invented Cookies?" (Kindergarten, Week 10: Food), "Ready" (1st Grade, Week 1: School), "Explorer" (3rd Grade, Week 23: Exploring), "Crossing the International Date Line" (4th Grade, Week 34: On the Move); copyright ©2012 by Joan Bransfield Graham. Used with permission of the author. All rights reserved.

John Grandits: "The Way You Sound" (4th Grade, Week 13: Families); copyright ©2012 by John Grandits. Used with permission of the author. All rights reserved.

Nikki Grimes: "Riddle" (4th Grade, Week 15: Stuff We Love), "Waiting" (5th Grade, Week 13: Families); copyright ©2012 by Nikki Grimes. Used with permission of the author. All rights reserved.

Lorie Ann Grover: "Waiting" (Kindergarten, Week 20: Art & Colors), "Fifty Yard Dash" (4th Grade, Week 2: More School); copyright ©2012 by Lorie Ann Grover. Used with permission of Curtis Brown, Ltd. All rights reserved.

Monica Gunning: "Saturdays" (4th Grade, Week 14: Community), "A Real Bed" (5th Grade, Week 12: House & Home); copyright ©2012 by Monica Gunning. Used with permission of the author. All rights reserved.

Mary Lee Hahn: "Bluejay Sings Two Different Songs" (Kindergarten, Week 8: In the Air); copyright ©2012 by Mary Lee Hahn. Used with permission of the author. All rights reserved.

Avis Harley: "My Kindergarten Choir" (Kindergarten; Week 16: Holidays), "Litter's Littlest" (1st Grade, Week 5: More Pets), "Last Try" (1st Grade, Week 31: Different Forms), "Recess" (2nd Grade, Week 2: More School), "Catching a Yawn" (3rd Grade, Week 18: Human Body), "A Branch of Friendship" (4th Grade, Week 21: Love & Friendship); copyright ©2012 by Avis Harley. Used with permission of the author. All rights reserved.

David L. Harrison: "Oh Man!" (Kindergarten, Week 5: More Pets), "No Way!" (Kindergarten, Week 35: Summer Vacation), "My Pet" (2nd Grade, Week 4: Pets); copyright ©2012 by David L. Harrison. Used with permission of the author. All rights reserved.

Terry Webb Harshman: "Tadpole Wishes" (Kindergarten, Week 7: In the Water), "Cabbage House" (Kindergarten, Week 12: House & Home), "Underwear Scare" (1st Grade, Week 2: More School), "Clay Time" (1st Grade, Week 20: Art & Colors), "Little Village" (3rd Grade, Week 16: Holidays), "Global Gorging" (4th Grade, Week 10: Food); copyright ©2012 by Terry Webb Harshman. Used with permission of the author. All rights reserved.

Juanita Havill: "I Might Go to Mars" (2nd Grade, Week 28: Books), "Car Trip" (3rd Grade, Week 34: On the Move), "Moon Buggy" (3rd Grade, Week 36: Looking Forward), "Wheel of Progress" (5th Grade, Week 24: Science & Technology); copyright ©2012 by Juanita Havill. Used with permission of the author. All rights reserved.

Georgia Heard: "The Winner" (2nd Grade, Week 3: Fun & Games), "Stapler" (3rd Grade, Week 33: Personification); copyright ©2012 by Georgia Heard. Used with permission of the author. All rights reserved.

Esther Hershenhorn: "The Writer's Drill" (3rd Grade, Week 30: Rhyme, Repetition, & Rhythm), "Super Key Man" (4th Grade, Week 24: Science & Technology); copyright ©2012 by Esther Hershenhorn. Used with permission of the author. All rights reserved.

Sara Holbrook: "Bubble Bath" (Kindergarten, Week 15: Stuff We Love), "The Library" (2nd Grade, Week 1: School), "Fire Station" (2nd Grade, Week 14: Community); copyright ©2012 by Sara Holbrook. Used with permission of the author. All rights reserved.

Carol-Ann Hoyte: "It's a Wrap" (3rd Grade, Week 19: More Human Body), "Vacation Communication" (3rd Grade, Week 24: Science & Technology), "From Root to Tip" (5th Grade, Week 19: More Human Body); copyright ©2012 by Carol-Ann Hoyte. Used with permission of the author. All rights reserved.

Patricia Hubbell: "Happy Song for the First Day of School" (Kindergarten, Week 1: School), "My Dog Jack Thinks Up His Valentine" (2nd Grade, Week 21: Love & Friendship), "Poem Like the Sea (3rd Grade, Week 29: Poetry Poems), "Feeling Jumpy" (4th Grade, Week 1: School); copyright ©2012 by Patricia Hubbell. Used with permission of the author. All rights reserved.

Jacqueline Jules: "Embarrassed" (1st Grade, Week 22: A Kinder Place), "Running Back" (4th Grade, Week 3: Fun & Games); copyright ©2012 by Jacqueline Jules. Used with permission of the author. All rights reserved.

Bobbi Katz: "Ingredients for a Valentine" (1st Grade, Week 21: Love & Friendship), "When the Future Arrives" (5th Grade, Week 36: Looking Forward); copyright ©2012 by Bobbi Katz. Used with permission of the author. All rights reserved.

X.J. Kennedy: "Bat" (1st Grade, Week 8: In the Air), "Armadillo" (1st Grade, Week 26: Nonsense), "Backyard Swing" (2nd Grade, Week 12: House & Home), "Eight-year-old Uncle" (3rd Grade, Week 26: Nonsense); copyright ©2012 by X. J. Kennedy. Used with permission of Curtis Brown, Ltd. All rights reserved.

Michele Krueger: "Recess" (3rd Grade, Week 2: More School); copyright ©2012 by Michele Krueger. Used with permission of the author. All rights reserved.

Julie Larios: "Who's Who" (Kindergarten, Week 13: Families), "My Bike" (Kindergarten, Week 32: Metaphor and Simile), "Outer Spaceman" (2nd Grade, Week 32: Metaphor and Simile), "A Plague of Penguins" (3rd Grade, Week 4: Pets), "Pirate Parrot" (4th Grade, Week 5: More Pets); copyright ©2012 by Julie Larios. Used with permission of the author. All rights reserved.

Irene Latham: "Summer Storm" (4th Grade, Week 33: Personification), "Backpack" (5th Grade, Week 2: More School); copyright ©2012 by Irene Latham. Used with permission of the author. All rights reserved.

JonArno Lawson: "Gift Ungiven" (4th Grade, Week 16: Holidays); copyright ©2012 by JonArno Lawson. Used with permission of the author. All rights reserved.

Gail Carson Levine: "You Misbehave" (5th Grade, Week 21: Love & Friendship); copyright ©2012 by Gail Carson Levine. Used with permission of Curtis Brown, Ltd. All rights reserved.

Constance Levy: "No Wonder" (Kindergarten, Week 33: Personification), "Lucky Penny" (3rd Grade, Week 15: Stuff We Love), "Bird Alert: Storm-Warning!" (4th Grade, Week 8: In the Air), "Avocado" (4th Grade, Week 11: More Food); copyright ©2012 by Constance Levy. Used with permission of the author. All rights reserved.

Debbie Levy: "Crunch" (2nd Grade, Week 10: Food), "My Best Friend Is Leaving" (3rd Grade, Week 35: Summer Vacation); copyright ©2012 by Debbie Levy. Used with permission of the author. All rights reserved.

J. Patrick Lewis: "Frog and Toad" (Kindergarten, Week 21: Love & Friendship), "Gnat and Flea" (1st Grade, Week 27: World of Words), "Lizard and Chameleon" (2nd Grade, Week 20: Art & Colors), "Honey" (3rd Grade, Week 32: Metaphor & Simile), "Why Hippos Look Baked" (4th Grade, Week 26: Nonsense); copyright ©2012 by J. Patrick Lewis. Used with permission of Curtis Brown, Ltd. All rights reserved.

George Ella Lyon: "Tree I Leaned Against" (1st Grade, Week 6: On the Ground), "Christmas Is" (2nd Grade, Week 16: Holidays); copyright ©2012 by George Ella Lyon. Used with permission of the author. All rights reserved.

Guadalupe Garcia McCall: "Bailes" (4th Grade, Week 17: Time Together), "Doña Pepita" (5th Grade, Week 14: Community), "The Bully" (5th Grade, Week 22: A Kinder Place); copyright ©2012 by Guadalupe Garcia McCall. Used with permission of the author. All rights reserved.

Heidi Mordhorst: "Funday, Imaginary 1st" (3rd Grade, Week 1: School), "Things are looking up" (5th Grade, Week 33: Personification); copyright ©2012 by Heidi Mordhorst. Used with permission of the author. All rights reserved.

Kenn Nesbitt: "My Porcupine Is Feeling Fine" (4th Grade, Week 4: Pets); copyright ©2012 by Kenn Nesbitt. Used with permission of the author. All rights reserved.

Lesléa Newman: "By the Sea" (1st Grade, Week 35: Summer Vacation), "Half-Past Never" (2nd Grade, Week 26: Nonsense), "Rough and Tumble" (2nd Grade, Week 30: Rhyme, Repetition, & Rhythm), "I've Never Seen a Purple Cow" (4th Grade, Week 20: Art & Colors), "Greetings" (5th Grade, Week 17: Time Together); copyright ©2012 by Leslea Newman. Used with permission of the author. All rights reserved.

Linda Sue Park: "Photo Op" (1st Grade, Week 16: Holidays), "Two Scoops" (3rd Grade, Week 10: Food); copyright ©2012 by Linda Sue Park. Used with permission of Curtis Brown, Ltd. All rights reserved.

Ann Whitford Paul: "Crayons" (Kindergarten, Week 31: Different Forms), "Crocodile" (1st Grade, Week 7: In the Water), "What's the Opposite..." (5th Grade, Week 4: Pets); copyright ©2012 by Ann Whitford Paul. Used with permission of the author. All rights reserved.

Greg Pincus: "First" (1st Grade, Week 28: Books), "Bubble Gum" (2nd Grade, Week 15: Stuff We Love); copyright ©2012 by Greg Pincus. Used with permission of the author. All rights reserved.

Jack Prelutsky: "The World's Most Ancient Ant" (Kindergarten, Week 6: On the Ground), "Once a Week at Noon" (1st Grade, Week 30: Rhyme, Repetition, & Rhythm), "My Carrots Are Angry" (2nd Grade, Week 33: Personification), "A Clam" (3rd Grade, Week 7: In the Water), "My Kitchen Was Invaded" (3rd Grade, Week 12: House & Home), "The Kangarooster" (4th Grade, Week 30: Rhyme, Repetition, & Rhythm), "The World's Most Intelligent Chicken" (5th Grade, Week 1: School); copyright ©2012 by Jack Prelutsky. Used with permission of the author. All rights reserved.

Mary Quattlebaum: "Mud Supper" (1st Grade, Week 15: Stuff We Love), "Why Does Weather?" (2nd Grade, Week 9: Weather); copyright ©2012 by Mary Quattlebaum. Used with permission of the author. All rights reserved.

Heidi Bee Roemer: "Antarctica, AntarcticO!" (1st Grade, Week 23: Exploring), "Look It Up!" (3rd Grade, Week 27: World of Words), "The Guy in the Closet" (4th Grade, Week 19: More Human Body), "Flapjack Flip" (5th Grade, Week 11: More Food); copyright ©2012 by Heidi Bee Roemer. Used with permission of the author. All rights reserved.

Michael J. Rosen: "Centipede" (4th Grade, Week 36: Looking Forward), "Earthworms" (5th Grade, Week 6: On the Ground), "Funny Bone (Humerus)" (5th Grade, Week 18: Human Body); copyright ©2012 by Michael J. Rosen. Used with permission of the author. All rights reserved.

Deborah Ruddell: "How Big Is the Atlas Moth?" (2nd Grade, Week 8: In the Air), "The Last Day of School" (A Poem for Everyone); copyright ©2012 by Deborah Ruddell. Used with permission of the author. All rights reserved.

Laura Purdie Salas: "Petting Zoo" (Kindergarten, Week 4: Pets), "Fire!" (1st Grade, Week 14: Community), "Music Lesson" (2nd Grade, Week 25: Song & Dance), "Corn, Before the Butter" (4th Grade, Week 31: Different Forms), "How Is a Meadow an Ocean?" (5th Grade, Week 29: Poetry Poems), "House Mouse" (5th Grade, Week 31: Different Forms); copyright ©2012 by Laura Purdie Salas. Used with permission of the author. All rights reserved.

Michael Salinger: "I Sit On My Bottom" (Kindergarten, Week 19: More Human Body), "My Noisy Family" (3rd Grade, Week 17: Time Together); copyright ©2012 by Michael Salinger. Used with permission of the author. All rights reserved.

Ken Slesarik: "The Woodland Vole" (2nd Grade, Week 6: On the Ground), "Small Talk" (3rd Grade, Week 22: A Kinder Place); copyright ©2012 by Ken Slesarik. Used with permission of the author. All rights reserved.

Eileen Spinelli: "Poem for a Bully" (4th Grade, Week 22: A Kinder Place), "Today" (4th Grade, Week 29: Poetry Poems), "Get a Life" (5th Grade, Week 16: Holidays); copyright ©2012 by Eileen Spinelli. Used with permission of the author. All rights reserved.

Susan Marie Swanson: "Paint Mind" (5th Grade, Week 20: Art & Colors); copyright ©2012 by Susan Marie Swanson. Used with permission of the author. All rights reserved.

Amy Ludwig VanDerwater: "Tooth" (Kindergarten, Week 18: Human Body), "Baby Tooth" (1st Grade, Week 18: Human Body), "Vacation" (1st Grade, Week 36: Looking Forward), "Out My Window" (3rd Grade, Week 14: Community), "A Quiet Day" (3rd Grade, Week 28: Books); copyright ©2012 by Amy Ludwig VanDerwater. Used with permission of Curtis Brown, Ltd. All rights reserved.

Lee Wardlaw: "Catku" (3rd Grade, Week 31: Different Forms); copyright ©2012 by Lee Wardlaw. Used with permission of Curtis Brown, Ltd. All rights reserved.

Charles Waters: "Sack Lunch" (Kindergarten, Week 11: More Food), "My Dog" (1st Grade, Week 9: Weather), "Charm Bracelet" (5th Grade, Week 15: Stuff We Love); copyright ©2012 by Charles Waters. Used with permission of the author. All rights reserved.

April Halprin Wayland: "Appy Birthday" (2nd Grade, Week 24: Science & Technology), "I Had to Get a Shot at the Doctor's" (4th Grade, Week 18: Human Body), "How to Open the Attic Door" (5th Grade, Week 26: Nonsense); copyright ©2012 by April Halprin Wayland. Used with permission of the author. All rights reserved.

Carole Boston Weatherford: "Loose Tooth, Whose Tooth? (Kindergarten, Week 30: Rhyme, Repetition, & Rhythm), "Dreamland" (2nd Grade, Week 19: More Human Body), "Africa's Child" (2nd Grade, Week 23: Exploring); copyright ©2012 by Carole Boston Weatherford. Used with permission of the author. All rights reserved.

Steven Withrow: "Green Sea Turtle" (5th Grade, Week 7: In the Water); copyright ©2012 by Steven Withrow. Used with permission of the author. All rights reserved.

Allan Wolf: "The Most Glad-to-See Day of the Year" (A Poem for Everyone), "Let's Hop around Like Kangaroos" (Kindergarten, Week 3: Fun & Games), "How Many Slams Are in an Old Screen Door?" (Kindergarten, Week 26: Nonsense), "The Secret of the Clouds" (1st Grade, Week 33: Personification), "The Secret Seed" (2nd Grade, Week 36: Looking Forward), "The Front Yard Where the Maple Tree Stands" (4th Grade, Week 12: House & Home), "Family Vacation" (5th Grade, Week 35: Summer Vacation); copyright ©2012 by Allan Wolf. Used with permission of the author. All rights reserved.

Janet Wong: "Something I Did" (Kindergarten, Week 22: A Kinder Place), "Moving Up Day" (Kindergarten, Week 36: Looking Forward), "Grandfather's Chopsticks" (1st Grade, Week 11: More Food), "Watching Football" (1st Grade, Week 17: Time Together), "Skype" (1st Grade, Week 24: Science & Technology), "Double the Trouble" (2nd Grade, Week 13: Families), "Momma's Trying" (2nd Grade, Week 18: Human Body), "Pick-Up Truck" (2nd Grade, Week 34: On the Move), "Fishing" (3rd Grade, Week 3: Fun & Games), "The Breakfast Boss" (3rd Grade, Week 13: Families), "The Do Kind" (3rd Grade, Week 21: Love & Friendship), "Directions" (5th Grade, Week 34: On the Move); copyright ©2012 by Janet Wong. Used with permission of the author. All rights reserved.

Jane Yolen: "Pumpkin" (3rd Grade, Week 11: More Food), "Humpback Whale" (4th Grade, Week 7: In the Water), "First Take" (5th Grade, Week 27: World of Words); copyright ©2012 by Jane Yolen. Used with permission of Curtis Brown, Ltd. All rights reserved.

TGIF!

We hope that you are finding Fridays even more special now that you're taking a few minutes each week to share a poem with your students on Poetry Friday. Spending time together with a funny, thoughtful, or interesting poem is a terrific way to develop a classroom community, talk about our feelings and experiences, and learn new words and concepts. And if you've shared 36 poems—one per week throughout the school year—we hope it has also become a beloved tradition.

Have you been marking up this book with notes about your favorite poems and strategies for sharing poetry? If not, go back and do that now. Add whatever you remember about students' responses to individual poems. We want this book to become one of the most useful resources in your professional library—as well as one of your favorite books for sharing aloud.

Wouldn't it be wonderful if this Poetry Friday experience was part of every grade level for every student? What a culture of literacy and language love that would create! **Please help us spread the word about the power of poetry** and ensure that every child has a chance to experience these fabulous five minutes every Friday!

ABOUT THIS BOOK

"Poetry can rhyme or not, speak to deep emotions, or lift us with light language and witty wordplay. **What teacher wouldn't want to inspire their students** *to aspire to write and read poetry as a daily practice?"*

⧏⧐ Lisa Von Drasek ⧏⧐

Acknowledgments

Janet likes to call us "poetry evangelists." At the same time, though, she sometimes wonders if we are preaching to the choir about the glory of poetry.

This book represents an effort to reach beyond the choir—to preach poetry on the street corner. We hope that this book inspires teachers who are new to poetry or who haven't read much poetry in years. If you liked this book, please tell the world—or at least your colleagues in your school and school district. If any of your fellow teachers are not in the habit of sharing poetry, those are the people we need you to talk to first!

This is our most ambitious poetry adventure yet, our first effort in blending poetry and teaching with 218 original poems and curriculum connections for every poem.

We cannot praise enough the generosity of the community of poets who write for young people. This is an extraordinary group, and we continue to be humbled by their willingness to participate in our projects. The poets who contributed to our PoetryTagTime trio of digital anthologies and to this book as well are the best in our field. Please get to know them and their books on their individual pages in the Meet the Poets sections at our website.

A final note: our sincere thanks to our readers and book buyers and book sharers for their support. Please visit our blogs and continue to spread the word about our books!

With deepest appreciation,

Sylvia and Janet

www.PomeloBooks.com
www.PoetryTagTime.com
PoetryFridayAnthology.Blogspot.com

About Sylvia Vardell

Sylvia M. Vardell is Professor in the School of Library and Information Studies at Texas Woman's University and has taught graduate courses in children's and young adult literature at various universities since 1981. Vardell has published extensively, including five books on literature for children, as well as over 20 book chapters and 100 journal articles. Her current work focuses on poetry for children, including a regular blog, *PoetryforChildren,* since 2006. She is also the regular "Everyday Poetry" columnist for ALA's *Book Links* magazine.

Vardell has served as a member or chair of several national award committees including the NCTE Award for Poetry, the NCTE Notables, the Cybils Poetry Award, the ALA Odyssey Award for audiobooks, the ALA Sibert Award for informational literature, and the NCTE Orbis Pictus Award for nonfiction, among others. She has conducted over 100 presentations at state, regional, national, and international conferences, and has received grants from the Young Adult Library Service Association (YALSA), Ezra Jack Keats Foundation, National Council of Teachers of English (NCTE), the Assembly on Literature for Young Adults Foundation, the Texas Library Association, and the National Endowment for the Humanities. She taught at the University of Zimbabwe in Africa as a Fulbright scholar and is a consultant to the Poetry Foundation.

Other Professional Books by Sylvia Vardell

Poetry Aloud Here: Sharing Poetry with Children (2012)

The Poetry Teacher's Book of Lists (2012)

Children's Literature in Action: A Librarian's Guide (2008)

Poetry People: A Practical Guide to Children's Poets (2007)

Literature-based Instruction with English Language Learners (2002; with Nancy Hadaway and Terrell Young)

About Janet Wong

Janet S. Wong is a graduate of Yale Law School and former lawyer who switched careers and became a children's poet. Her dramatic career change has been featured on *The Oprah Winfrey Show*, CNN's *Paula Zahn Show*, and *Radical Sabbatical*. She is the author of 30 books for children and teens on a wide variety of subjects, including writing and revision (*You Have to Write*), creative recycling (*The Dumpster Diver*), diversity and community (*Apple Pie 4th of July*), cheating on tests (*Me and Rolly Maloo*), and chess (*Alex and the Wednesday Chess Club*).

Wong has served as a member of several national committees including the NCTE Award for Poetry, the NCTE Commission on Literature, the Notable Books for a Global Society committee of the International Reading Association (IRA), the SCBWI Golden Kite committee (for picture books), and the PEN Center USA Literary Award committee (for children's literature). Wong is a frequent featured or keynote speaker at conferences and has worked with over 200,000 children at schools all over the world. Her recent focus is the exploration of digital opportunities for children's books. She encourages children not just to read e-books, but also to publish their own writing using affordable new technologies.

Selected Poetry Books by Janet Wong

Declaration of Interdependence: Poems for an Election Year (2012)

Once Upon A Tiger: New Beginnings for Endangered Animals (2011)

TWIST: Yoga Poems (2007)

Knock on Wood: Poems about Superstitions (2003)

Behind the Wheel: Poems about Driving (1999)

The Rainbow Hand: Poems about Mothers and Children (1999)

A Suitcase of Seaweed (1996)

Good Luck Gold (1994)

THE POETRY FRIDAY ANTHOLOGY Series for K-5 and Middle School

Spring 2014

K-5 Edition

Middle School Edition (grades 6–8)

Science Edition (grades K-5)

"Savvy teachers have learned they can trust Vardell and Wong . . . THE essential resource for allowing poetry to assume its rightful, thoughtful place in today's classroom."

—Barbara Ward, IRA's Reading Today

More from Pomelo Books

Share The PoetryTagTime Trio—***PoetryTagTime***, ***P*TAG***, and ***Gift Tag***—the first-ever e-book anthologies of original poetry for children and teens.

These books are ideal for projecting on a screen and sharing with your whole class in a participatory reading. Keep your Poetry Friday tradition going strong!

pomelo ✳ books